How To Repair Old-Time Radios

Other TAB books by the author:

No. 1108 *Lasers, The Light Fantastic*
No. 1199 *The Master IC Cookbook*

How To Repair Old-Time Radios
Clayton L. Hallmark

TAB BOOKS Inc.
BLUE RIDGE SUMMIT, PA. 17214

FIRST EDITION

THIRD PRINTING

Printed in the United States of America

Reproduction or publication of the content in any manner, without express
permission of the publisher, is prohibited. No liability is assumed with respect
to the use of the information herein.

Library of Congress Cataloging in Publication Data

Hallmark, Clayton.
    How to repair old-time radios.

    Includes index.
    1. Radio-Repairing—Amateurs' manuals.   I. Title.
TK9956.H32   621.3841'87   79-23251
ISBN 0-8306-9737-3
ISBN 0-8306-1148-7 pbk.

Preface

Don't give up on that broken-down relic of the golden years of radio. Just a few minor repairs or easy tube replacements can give it new life. That dusty forlorn-looking old radio in the secondhand shop or in your own attic or basement was made with a care and a quality of parts that would be prohibitively expensive today but you can restore it to good-as-new condition and turn it into a valuable collectible and useful source of entertainment.

And you don't have to be a radio expert to do it. You don't have to have a lot of expensive equipment either. Chances are you already have the tools and supplies you need to fix most sets. In some cases a VOM—an all-purpose electrical tester that can buy at any electronics store for a few dollars and learn to use in a few minutes—will come in handy but you may not even need that.

You will need some basic information however—the kind of practical nuts-and-bolts data you'll find in this book. This book is the culmination of years of experience in troubleshooting and repairing radio equipment and teaching others to do the same. It is as clear and simple and practical as I can make it. It is not a book on radio theory because I realize that the collector is more interested in getting a worthwhile old-time radio to work than in *how* it works. Some theory—perhaps a brief review of what you learned in high school physics about electronic tubes—will be useful and is included. But even this can be sugarcoated. Most of the theory you will need to know is presented as a history lesson rather than an electronics lesson. I have found that this chronological approach is not only more interesting and palatable to most persons it is also more logical, sensible and meaningful. Furthermore, the information thus learned is far more likely to be retained. But again, contrary to what you have thought you do not need to know any radio theory to fix most sets. In many cases all you need to know is which tube to unplug and replace and if it is a type no longer made, what other tube can replace it. That is the kind of practical matter in which you and I are interested.

One of the problems in servicing old-time radios is in replacing defective and nonavailable parts with present-day items. Many of the tubes used in the old sets have not been manufactured for many years, but there are quite a few types that can be replaced with currently manufactured tubes with no wiring changes. Other obsolete tubes can be replaced with other types of the same era. To help you with these substitutions, I have included a "Mini Manual of Out-of-Date Tubes" virtually a book within a book which provides complete data on the old all-numbers types (00-A to 864) as well as the early "standard" types (such as the 2A5 and 6A7).

Of course, a radio set is more than just tubes so I have also provided specific practical information about checking other parts—sometimes using just your senses, such as sight, touch and smell. I have also included full particulars on replacing, repairing, substituting, and reconstructing the other parts that go to make up a radio. I have done this for just about every part except the cabinet, whose refinishing and repair is along the same lines as for an antique or collectible furniture.

If you are new to the hobby of collecting antique radios, I bid you welcome. If you are new to the rewarding work of repairing them, I wish you luck. As a collector and restorer of antique radios, you will be working to preserve a priceless piece of our technological heritage. I am proud to help.

Clayton L. Hallmark

Contents

Chapter 1
The Pioneers and Their Creations

The development of the electron tube and its associated communication circuits was not the work of any one scientist. Rather it was the cumulative result of the researches, discoveries, and inventions of numerous investigators. Actually, to trace the very beginnings of certain important discoveries, which later led to fruitful results, would necessitate a discussion beyond the scope of this book. However, for all practical purposes, modern radio art may be said to have had its beginnings toward the end of the last century when, in 1883, Thomas A. Edison was experimenting with his newly invented incandescent lamp.

The Edison incandescent lamp may be regarded, in a sense, as the forerunner or prototype of the modern electron tube. Edison noticed that the carbon wire filament of these first incandescent lamps burned out at the point at which the filament entered the glass bulb. Looking for an explanation, he inserted a second conductor or *plate* into the lamp (this is basically the structure of the *diode,* or two-electrode tube of today), and recorded in his notebook that this *dead end* wire or plate, when connected through a current meter to the positive side of the battery, showed a flow of current (Fig. 1-1) across the space between the filament and the plate. Normally, such an arrangement constituted an open circuit; therefore, current flow, according to the knowledge of electrical circuits at that time, was regarded as an impossibility, for here was an *open circuit.* Edison could find no satisfactory explanation for this phenomenon, which became known as the *Edison effect.*

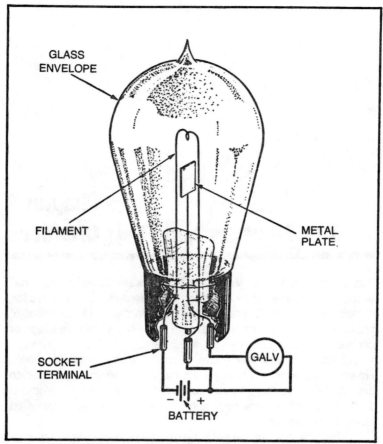

Fig. 1-1. Circuit of Edison's 2-electrode tube.

An accurate and epoch-making explanation of the Edison effect was advanced in 1899 by a British scientist, Sir J. J. Thomson. He presented the theory that small, negative particles of electricity, called *electrons*, were emitted by the filament in Edison's lamp as a result of operating it at incandescence or white heat. He said, further, that these electrons, because of their negative charge, were attracted to the positively charged plate. Thus, as long as the filament was heated to the proper temperature, electrons would flow from it to the plate. This movement of electrons constituted a flow of electron current, and the electron stream was the means by which the gap was bridged across the intervening space between the filament and the plate, thus closing the circuit.

Thomson's findings came to be known as the *electron theory*. Briefly, this theory views the atoms of all matter as being composed of infinitesimally small, individual negative particles, or electrons, held within the atom by the attraction of a central nucleus of positively charged particles called *protons*. Under suitable conditions, as by the application of heat to a substance, some of the electrons within the substance could be liberated. This extremely important theory gave great impetus to subsequent research and led to great developments in electron tubes.

Equipped with this knowledge, other scientists explored further. The next significant development of far-reaching importance was the work of J. A. Fleming, an English scientists, who designed the first practical electron tube. Fleming observed from Edison's work that when the plate connection was made to the

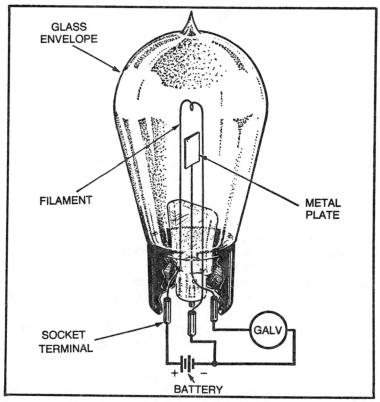

Fig. 1-2. With plate connected to negative side of battery, current through tube is negligible.

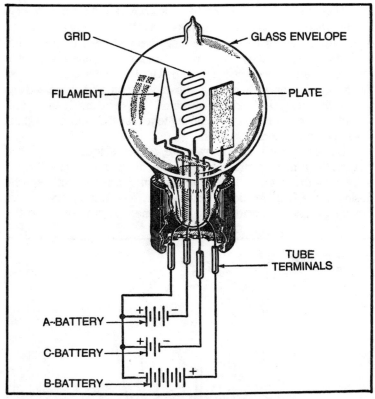

Fig. 1-3. Construction of DeForest's 3-element tube, or triode.

negative rather than to the positive side of the battery, the current was zero (Fig. 1-2). This property provided the basis for the operation of the electron tube as a *rectifier*; that is, as a device for the conversion of alternating current into direct current. Fleming, calling his modified version of Edison's two-electrode lamp a *valve* (the term still used for the electron tube in England), thereby provided a superior detector to supplant the comparatively insensitive crystal detector.

Fleming's valve was a two-electrode tube. For several years it was the only electron device in use. At this point it seemed that the progress of wireless communication had reached its practical limit, a limit determined by the existing methods and devices used for transmitting and receiving radio signals. The most powerful transmitters could transmit signals to receiving sets more than several hundred miles away, but the reception of such signals was undependable. The range and the dependability of radio communication could be increased only by the development of some method by which the weak signal could be amplified. A tube developed by Lee DeForest in 1907 supplied this needed means of amplification. Later improvements of this tube have made possible the reception of radio signals millions of times too weak to be audible without amplification.

DeForest, by inserting an extra electrode in the form of a few turns of fine wire between the filament and the plate of Fleming's valve, made the tube an *amplifier*. DeForest called the third electrode the *control grid*. It provided the desired amplification by virtue of the fact that relatively large plate current and voltage changes could be controlled by small variations of control-grid voltage without expenditure of appreciable power in the control circuit. DeForest called his three-electrode tube an *audion,* a designation superseded in present-day usage by the term *triode* (Fig. 1-3).

TUBE TYPES

Each kind of electron tube is generally capable of performing many different functions, and therefore initial classification of these tubes is not based on functions, but upon their physical construction (Fig. 1-4). The envelopes or housings are made of glass or metal or, in a few isolated cases, of both materials. The absence or presence of air or other gases in the envelope distinguishes the two fundamental classes of electron tubes. In the *vacuum* tube, all gases have been removed; in the *gaseous* tube, after all air has been removed, a small amount of mercury vapor or inert gas is placed within the envelope.

In all electron tubes, one electrode, called the *cathode*, is the emitter of electrons. The cathode must be heated to cherry red or to

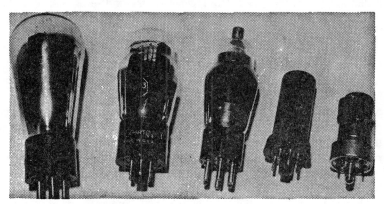

Fig. 1-4. Representative electron tubes.

incandescence before the electrons are freed from its surface to move across to the second electrode, or *anode*. In vacuum tubes, sometimes called *high-vacuum* or *hard-vacuum* tubes, the cathode is in every case—except the photoelectric tube—heated by some external source of power, and these tubes, therefore, are not distinguished as to type of cathode. In gaseous tubes, sometimes called *soft* tubes, a further subclassification is made into *hot-cathode* and *cold-cathode* types. In the first type, the cathode is heated to the proper temperature for emission by some external source of power; in the second type, the gas within the tube is ionized, and then the cathode is bombombarded by positive ions which raise the cathode to the correct emission temperature.

Both vacuum tubes and gaseous tubes of either the hot- or cold-cathode type are further classified as to the number of active elements or electrodes contained inside the envelope. The simplest of these, described above, contains two elements and is known as a *diode*. A tube which contains three elements is known as a *triode*, and a tube with four elements is called a *tetrode*. If it contains five elements it is a *pentode*. In each instance, the type classification indicates the number of elements in the tube. In the following sections each of these tubes is illustrated and the differences between them fully explained.

Diodes

The simplest type of electron tube is the *diode*. It consists of two elements or electrodes, one of which is an *emitter* of electrons and the other a *collector* of electrons. Both elements are enclosed in an envelope of glass or metal. Although this discussion revolves around the vacuum diode from which most of the air has been removed, it should be understood that gaseous diodes also exist. The term diode refers to the number of elements within the tube envelope rather than to any specific application. In this connection, the complete electron-emitting system is treated as one element. Different names are applied to the diode to indicate the specific function of the tube in any particular electrical circuit. As one example, the diode can change alternating current into direct current; it is then a *rectifier*, and the tube is named accordingly. Therefore, when discussing the basic diode, reference is made to the tube as a type, rather than to any of its applications.

The electron collector is called the *plate* and the electron emitter is called the *cathode*. Although the latter term more specifically applied to the indirectly heated type of emitter, whereas the directly

14

heated type of emitter is referred to as the *filament*, the term cathode usually is used regardless of the method of heating. This usage is not so odd as it may seem, since the majority of tubes in use today are of the indirectly heated type.

In directly heated tubes, the filament is of the general construction illustrated in Fig. 1-5, showing two typical filamentary cathodes. The type shown at the left is known as an *inverted V*, and that on the right as an *inverted W*. The filament is held in place within the tube envelope (glass or metal) by means of suitable metal supports firmly resting in the glass stem of the tube. It is suspended from the top of the tube by a metal support which allows for the expansion of the filament wire when heated. The filament voltage is applied across the prong terminals of the filament in the tube base. Figure 1-6 is a cross-sectional view of a simple diode tube, showing the internal construction, tube base and wiring.

In indirectly heated tubes, the cathode-heater design can be either of the two common types shown in Fig. 1-7. The heater wire is usually either U-shaped, as shown on the left in A, or it can be twisted throughout its length, as on the right in A. In indirectly heated tubes, the cathode is an oxide-coated cylindrical sleeve, usually of nickel, which enclosed the heater wire. The heater is insulated from the nickel sleeve by an Alundum coating on the heater wire or by passing the heater wire through fine parallel holes in an Alundum tube. In directly heated high-power tubes, the cathode heater is constructed of tungsten and thoriated tungsten, since high voltages tend to destroy oxide-coated cathodes.

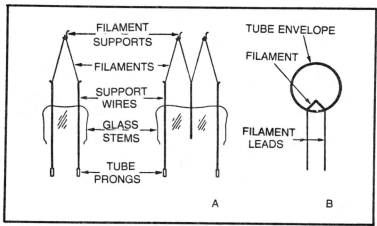

Fig. 1-5. Directly heated filments and schematic symbol.

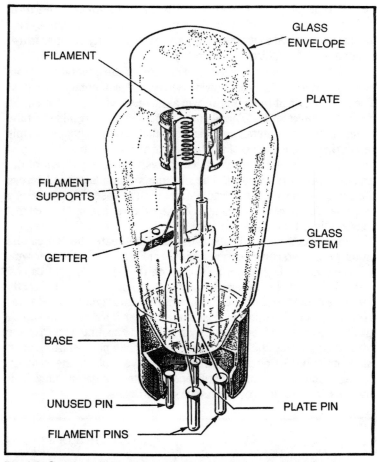

FILAMENT

GLASS
ENVELOPE

PLATE

FILAMENT
SUPPORTS

GLASS
STEM

GETTER

BASE

UNUSED PIN

PLATE PIN

FILAMENT PINS

Fig. 1-6. Cross-sectional view of simple half-wave diode of filament type.

The plate is usually of cylindrical construction, although frequently it has an elliptical form. Usually it surrounds its associated emitter, as in Fig. 1-6. The metals used for the diode plate (and the plates of most other tubes) usually are nickel, molybdenum, Monel Metal, or iron. A tube which contains one emitter and a single related plate is identified generally as a half-wave rectifier. Another name for tubes of this kind is simply *diode*.

Triodes

The invention of the *triode* or three-element tube, was one of the most important steps in modern electronics. Up to 1907 the diode was the only electron tube used in the primitive wireless communication systems of that time. In that year Forest disclosed his third element, an electrode which was added to the diode and so formed the triode. Not only did it modify the diode, but it opened a new era in communication facilities. DeForest's third element made present-day radio communication in all its forms a practical reality.

The emitter and the plate as used in the diode appear also in the triode. They retain their functions as a source of electrons and a collector of electrons, respectively. In the space between them, and located nearer to the emitter, is placed the third element, commonly called the *control grid*.

Fig.1-8, illustrating the organization of the cathode, control-grid, and plate electrodes of the triodes, is an example of the oval-shaped form of grid, and shows how the grid surrounds the emitter on all sides. The plate electrode is seen enveloping the control grid. Other examples of triode construction exist, but they do not differ greatly from this.

The dimensions and the shape of the electrodes used in triodes as well as the physical spacing between the electrodes, differ in accordance with the intended uses of the tubes. Since these are related to such details as the values of plate voltage and plate current, the elements of triodes used in transmitters generally are larger than those used in receivers.

The internal structure of the triode seldom is completely visible through the envelope. When the envelope is made of metal the reason is obvious. When the envelope is made of glass the view of

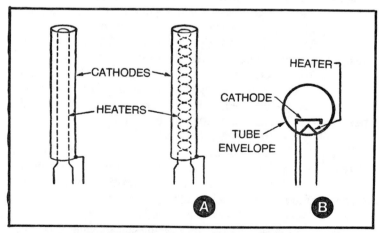

Fig. 1-7. Indirectly heated emitter and schematic symbol.

the inside usually is obscured because of the opaque coating formed by the *getter* when the tube is flashed—that is, heated to a high temperature. The getter is a substance that is placed within the envelope for the express purpose of absorbing any gases that may be liberated from the electrodes during initial operation. This keeps the vacuum created in the tube as high as possible. Magnesium is widely used as a getter, but other materials, such as barium, zirconium and phosphorous, also can be used.

The opaque deposit formed by the getter appears as a thin film on the lower half of the inside surface of the glass housing. The top usually remains transparent and some visual inspection of the electrodes inside is therefore possible. This is the usual means for determining whether the electron emitter is incandescent. In the larger transmitting tubes the getter coating usually does not obscure the metal parts inside the tube.

Tetrodes

Although the triode is an important device in communications, its use in amplifying systems is limited in some respects. The principal reason is the interelectrode capacitance between its electrodes, especially the capacitance between the control grid and the plate. As the frequency of operation is increased, the grid-plate capacitance affords an easier path for the transfer of energy back from the output to the input circuit. This action is most pronounced in a resonant system in which the grid and plate circuits are tuned to the same or similar frequencies. The result is that triode tubes seldom are used as amplifiers without recourse to special neutralizing systems to counterbalance the undesired feedback.

Neutralization is not wholly satisfactory. The higher the frequency of operation, the more critical is the adjustment. Sometimes it is impossible to neutralize properly over the entire band. Above all, neutralization is a critical adjustment and, frequently, a bothersome one. Its use was reduced by the development of new tube types which obviate neutralization by greatly reducing the interelectric grip-plate capacitance as a feedback path.

In addition to the problems of feedback, the triode does not satisfy all the amplifying needs encountered in receivers, transmitters, and related apparatus. The physical relationship among the electrodes of the triode is such as to set unsatisfactory limits on the degree of amplification that can be achieved in a practical lube. At one time this posed a serious problem for design engineers because

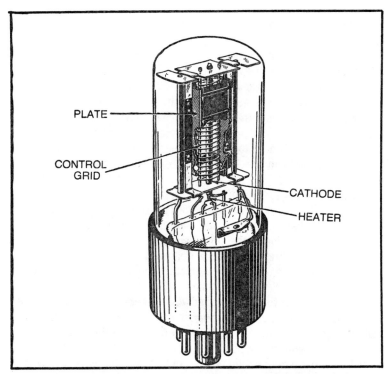

PLATE

CONTROL
GRID

CATHODE

HEATER

Fig. 1-8. Construction of triode, showing cathole, control-grid, and plate arrangement.

progress in communication depended on increasing the amplifying capabilities of equipment.

The answer was found in two types of tubes. Both are based on the triode but represent modifications of the original three-element electron tube. One of the versions is the *tertrode* or four-electrode electron tube, which contains an electron emitter, two grids, and a plate. The other is the *pentode*, which contains five electrodes, an electron emitter, three grids and a plate.

The development of electron tubes since the early 1920's resulted in more than just the multielectrode tetrode and pentode. Other tubes which have been developed are various combinations of diodes, triodes, tetrodes and pentodes in the same envelope. These are identified by the general name of *multiunit* tubes.

The four-electrode tube contains all the electrodes of the triode (with generally similar functions) and, in addition, a fourth electrode. This is the *screen grid*. As a rule, the four-electrode tube is called a tetrode, although upon occasion it is referred to as a screen-grid tube.

The physical organization of the tetrode (Fig. 1-9) does not differ too much from that of the triode. In A, the screen grid of the tetrode (type 48) is rectangular in shape. The plate is fine-shaped for heat dissipation purposes. In B, the outer screen grid is a perforated-metal structure of circular shape (type 32), located between the glass envelope and the plate electrode. The inner screen grid is oval and is located between the control grid and plate. There is variation in the shape of the grids; in some instances a helical form is used. The functioning of the electrodes is fundamentally the same regardless of the shape.

C and D show external views of two tetrodes. The tubes are substantially alike in appearance, but differ in one respect. The practice of using pins in the tube base as connecting points to the electrodes inside the envelope is followed in the tetrode, but an exception is the use of a metal connecting cap on the top of the tube. Tubes which have electrodes connected to portions of the envelope in addition to the base are called *double-ended* tubes. If *all* the electrodes appear as pins or prongs in the base of the tube, they are called *single-ended* tubes. In some tetrodes designed for use in receivers and similar lowpower equipment, the cap illustrated in C affords electrical connection to the control grid. The plate, screen-grid and heater (or filament) junctions are made through the tube base pins. In some higher-power tubes, such as are used in transmitters, the cap furnishes electrical contact wth the plate electrode, as in D. The remaining tube electrodes terminate at the base pins. The reason for cap connections to the control grid or to the plate, as the case may be, is the desire to reduce the capacitance between the connecting pin terminations of the control grid and the plate.

It is common practice to use the full names, such as control grid and screen grid, but for tube schematics it is advantageous to designate these electrodes in abbreviated form as G1 and G2. The smaller number is assigned to the grid which is closer to the cathode, this being the control grid. Therefore, G2 represents the screen grid. These notations are included in two schematic representations (Fig. 1-10). The old tube symbol, in A, finds little use in modern literature. B shows the modern tube symbol. It also is interesting to note that abridgement of the words screen grid to the single word screen, as meaning the same thing, is practiced regularly. When illustrated schematically with operating voltages applied to all the electrodes, the tetrode appears as in Fig. 1-11. The main difference

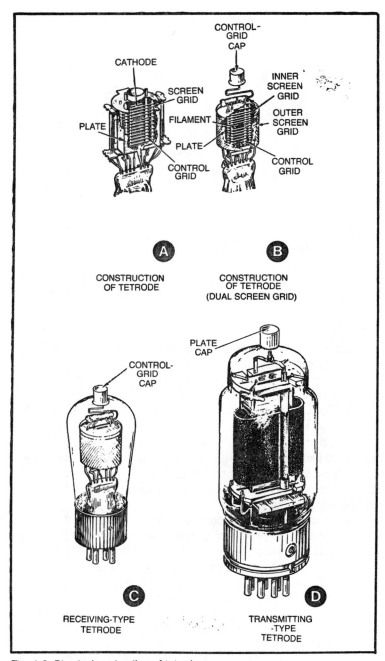

CATHODE

SCREEN GRID

PLATE

FILAMENT

PLATE

CONTROL GRID

CONTROL- GRID CAP

INNER SCREEN GRID

OUTER SCREEN GRID

CONTROL GRID

A

CONSTRUCTION OF TETRODE

B

CONSTRUCTION OF TETRODE (DUAL SCREEN GRID)

PLATE CAP

CONTROL- GRID CAP

C

RECEIVING-TYPE TETRODE

D

TRANSMITTING -TYPE TETRODE

Fig. 1-9. Physical contruction of tetrodes.

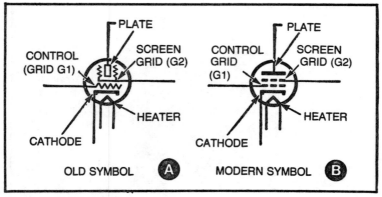

Fig. 1-10. Tube symbols for tetrode.

between the tetrode and the triode is the screen circuit and the source of its operating voltage. In normal use, the screen is made positive relative to the cathode by receiving a voltage from source Ebb, which also supplies the plate voltage. In the majority of instances, the DC screen voltage is appreciably less than the DC plate voltage.

Pentodes

The *pentode* is a five-electrode electron tube. It contains an emitter, three grids and a plate. The grid closest to the cathode, G1, is the control grid; next is the screen grid, G2; and the third, located between the screen grid and the plate, is the new *suppressor grid*, G3. The construction of a metal-type pentode is shown in Fig. 1-12. Symbolized, the pentode is shown in Fig. 1-13.

Functionally speaking, the action of the emitter, control grid, screen grid and plate in the pentode are the same as in the tetrode except that, whereas the tetrode suffers from negative-resistance effects, the pentode is free from these because of the action of the suppressor grid.

In external appearance some pentodes resemble the tetrode. This similarity is so great, even to the use of control-grid or plate caps on the top of the tube envelope, that identification by visual inspection is difficult. Three receiving-type pentodes are shown in Fig. 1-14. The envelope of a pentode may be glass, as in A, or metal. A departure from the tetrode appearance is the acorn-type tube shown in B. This is a comparatively small tube requiring a special socket and having wire extensions serving as the tube pins. Another physical feature of the acorn pentode is the location of the plate connection at the top and the control-grid connection at the bottom

22

of the envelope. These are stiff wires which protrude through the envelope. Another type of miniature tube is shown in C.

Multigrid Tubes

Tubes which have more than three grids commonly are referred to as multigrid tubes. For instance, if a grid is added to a pentode, a six-electric multigrid tube results. This tube is known as a *hexode*. The schematic symbol for an indirectly heated hexode is shown in A of Fig. 1-15. Other multigrid tubes are the *heptode*, shown in B, which contains five grids, and the *octode*, in C, which has six grids. In these tubes, as in the basic types, the grids are designated in numerical order starting with the control grid, as shown.

The hexode is an experimental tube and is never manufactured commercially. *Heptodes*, also known as pentagrid tubes because of their five grids, are used mostly in frequency converter or mixer circuits. When a heptode is used as a frequency converter, two voltages having different frequencies are each impressed on a separate grid of the tube. Heptodes also are used as volume compressors and expanders. In these applications the gain of an amplifier is controlled automatically. Just as the heptode, the octode also is used as a frequency converter.

Multiunit or Dual-Purpose Tubes

A multiunit or dual-purpose tube is one in which two or more individual tube-element structures are combined within a single envelope. As a result, compactness, economy and more satisfactory operation for certain purposes are achieved. The most commonly used multiunit tubes, known as duo-diodes and duo-triodes, combine

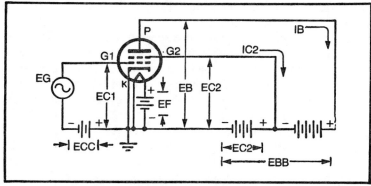

Fig. 1-11. Circuit representation of tetrode.

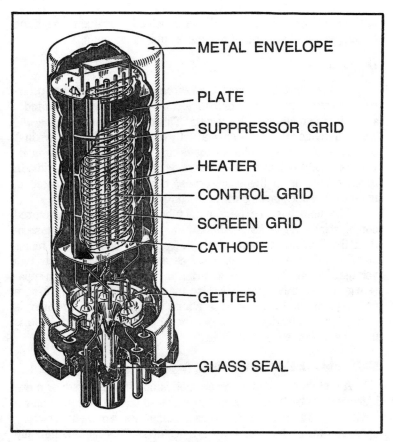

Fig. 1-12. Physical construction of pentode.

two diode or two triode elements. Frequently, a single common cathode is used which supplies electrons to both sets of elements in the multiunit tube. Occasionally, an electrode of one set of elements is connected internally to an electrode of another set of elements.

There are many types of multiunit tubes, used for a wide variety of purposes. The schematic symbols of the most common ones are shown in Fig. 1-16. The tube whose symbol is shown in A can be used as a full-wave rectifier, an FM (frequency-modulated) discriminator, or a combination detector and AVC (automatic volume control) rectifier. The diode-triode, in B, can be used as a diode detector and a triode amplifier. The duo-triode, in E, is used as a push-pull amplifier, two amplifiers in cascade, or as a special type of complex-wave generator. The triode-hexode, in L, and the triode-

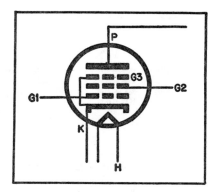

Fig. 1-13. Symbol of pentode.

heptode, in M, are used as mixer-oscillators superheterodyne receivers.

Table 1-1 lists typical examples of multipurpose tubes to be found in receiving-type equipment. The letters in the first column refer to the symbols used in Fig. 1-16.

Magic Tuning Eye

Electron-ray indicators (Fig. 1-19) are widely used in radio receivers to indicate proper tuning. Most indicator, or magic eye, tubes contain two sets of elements, one of which is a triode amplifier. The other section is a cathode-ray indicator.

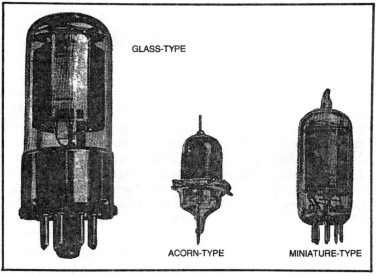

GLASS-TYPE

ACORN-TYPE   MINIATURE-TYPE

Fig. 1-14. Different types of receiving pentodes.

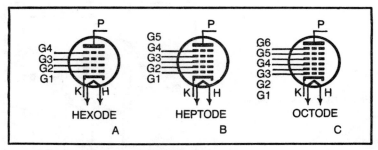

Fig. 1-15. Schematic symbols of multigrid tubes.

The electrons emitted by the cathode strike the conical plate, or target. This target is coated with a fluorescent paint that glows under the impact of the electrons. A small wire electrode called the ray-control electrode is parallel and close to the cathode. It deflects some of the electrons emitted from the cathode, producing a shadow on the target. This shadow is wedge-shaped, and the angle of the wedge varies with the voltage on the ray-control electrode. The plate of the internal triode amplifier is connected to the ray-control electrode, and therefore the shadow angle varies with the negative voltage applied to the grid of this triode. When the ray-control electrode is at the same potential as the target, the shadow closes completely. If the ray-control electrode is less positive than the plate, a shadow appears which is proportional in size to the difference in voltage. Since the voltage on the electrode is the same as that of the internal triode plate, the shadow angle increases with a more positive grid voltage.

SOCKETS FOR TUBES

The various types of electron tubes just discussed all must have some means of applying potentials and making connections to the various electrodes within the envelope. The external leads take the form of tube prongs, pins or caps. Usually, a group of prongs or pins is built into a tube base. The base material often is Bakelite, although other insulating materials are used. Sometimes the connecting leads take the form of pins which are built into the tube envelope itself. Occasionally, metal caps are bonded to the tube envelope, and the tube electrodes are connected to these caps through the envelope. The specific method used depends on the particular tube involved.

The early triode receiving tubes used a four-prong base. Two of these prongs were connected internally to the filament, and the other two were connected to the grid and the plate. The two filament

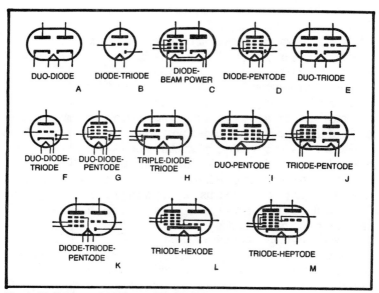

Fig. 1-16. Tube symbols for multiunit tubes.

prongs were slightly larger in diameter than the other prongs, so
that the tube could be inserted properly in a corresponding four-hole
socket. It is necessary to insert the tube properly so that the proper
operating voltages can be applied to the correct electrodes. Unless
some such method is used to *key* the tube, it can be damaged by
improper placement in its socket. Other methods have been used to
key the four-pin base. One method involves the use of a small metal
projection on the tube base which permits the tube to be inserted in
its socket in only one manner. Another method is to arrange the base
pins in such a pattern that the tube can be inserted into its socket in
only one way.

Table 1-1. Examples of multipurpose tubes in receivers.

symbol designation	multipurpose tube	examples of tube types
A	Duo-diode	5U4. 5V4. 6AL5. 6X5. 12LA5
B	Diode-triode	1H5. 1LH4
C	Diode-beam power	70L7. 117L7. 117N7.117P7
D	Diode-pentode	1N6. 1T6. 6SF7. 12A7.12SF7
E	Duo-triode	1J6. 6J6. 6N7. 6NS7.6SL7. 12AT7. 12AU7
F	Duo-diode-triode	1H5. 6AQ7. 6SQ7. 6V7. 7K7. 7X7. 12SQ7
G	Duo-diode-pentode	1F6. 7R7. 14E7. 14R7
H	Triple-diode-triode	6S8. 6T8. 12S8
I	Duo-pentode	1E7
J	Triode-pentode	6AD7. 6P7. 25B8
K	Diode-triode-pentode	3A8
L	Triode-hexode	6K8. 12K8
M	Triode-heptode	7J7. 7S7. 14J7

With the advent of more complex tubes, it became necessary to add more connecting pins to the tube base. The five, six, seven, eight and nine-pin bases were introduced. All of these bases are keyed by means of special fttings on the tube base which permit the tube to be inserted in the socket only one way (Fig. 1-17).

One of the most widely used of these multipin bases for receiving tubes is the eight-pin or *octal* base. In this base all the pins have the same diameter, and they are uniformly spaced. However, at the center of the base is an insulating post which has a vertical ridge. This acts as a key or guide pin which fits in a keyway in the tube socket. Thus, the tube can be inserted in only one way. The original idea of the octal socket was to have similar electrodes of any type of tube connected to the same pins, so that some degree of standardization would result. If any of the pins are not used they are left off the base, or no connection is made to them.

A variation of the octal base is used with *lock-in* receiving tubes. The base of such tubes also has eight pins. However, the contact pins are sealed directly into the glass envelope and no insulating base is used. The bottom portion of the envelope is fitted with a metal shell and a metal key or guide pin. This guide pin has a vertical ridge like the one used in the octal base. A groove around the bottom of the locating pin fits into a spring catch in the socket. This holds the tube firmly in the socket.

Another variation in the base of receiving tubes is used with miniature glass tubes. These tubes are used in modern electronic equipment because of their small size and many other desirable characteristics. Contact pins of these tubes are sealed directly into the glass envelope. Either seven or nine pins generally are used. Because of the additional spacing between two of these pins, the tubes cannot be inserted improperly in their sockets. Figure 1-18 illustrates six different types of electron-tube bases and their corresponding sockets.

Transmitting and special-purpose tubes use sockets and methods of connection which are subject to considerable variation. Some small transmitting tubes use a base structure similar to that used for receiving tubes. However, the larger types use special connections and terminals which are not at all standardized. Special high-frequency tubes use connection methods which conform with their special requirements. Cathode-ray tubes may use conventional octal sockets or sockets which have more than eight pins. A few commonly used bases for these tubes are the *magnal* (eleven-pin), *duaodecal* (twelve-pin), and the *diphetal* (fourteen-pin).

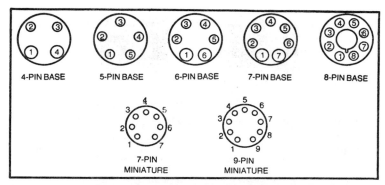

Fig. 1-17. Common electron-tube bases, showing arrangement of pins.

A standard system has been set up for numbering the base pins of the common tube bases. The pins are numbered consecutively in a *clockwise* direction looking up at the bottom of the tube base. When fewer than eight pins are required, the unnecessary ones are omitted and the spacing and the numbering of the remaining pins are unchanged. In the octal and lock-in-types, pin 1 is the pin directly clockwise of the ridge on the guide pin, as in Fig. 1-17. In the minature types, pin 1 is the clockwise pin of the two widely spaced pins. Other designations are shown in the figure.

Some attempts at electrode connection standardization were made by electron-tube manufacturers. These were only partly successful, because of the tremendous variety of tubes manufactured. A good many receiving tubes, however, do show a degree of uniformity in pin connections worth noting. For example, in the four-pin base, pins 1 and 4 usually are connected to the filament, pin 2 is connected to the plate, and pin 3 is connected to the control grid. In the five-pin base, pins 1 and 5 frequently are connected to the heater, pin 2 is connected to the plate, pin 3 is connected to the control grid, and pin 4 is connected to the cathode. When a five-pin base is used for a pentode tube, it is common practice to make the same connection as above except that the screen grid is connected to pin 3, and the control grid is connected to a grid cap at the top of the tube. The suppressor grid is connected internally to the cathode. In the six and seven-pin bases, pins 1 and 6 and pins 1 and 7 frequency are used as the heater connections. In the octal base, pin 1 usually is connected to the metal envelope or internal shield, pins 2 and 7 are connected to the heater, pin 3 is connected to the plate, pin 4 is connected to the screen grid, pin 5 is connected to the control grid, and pin 8 is connected to the cathode and the suppressor grid.

In the lock-in tube base, pins 1 and 8 usually are the heater connections. It must be emphasized that the wide variety of tube types makes it impossible to adhere rigidly to these pin connections.

HOW TUBES ARE NUMBERED

Every electron tube is identified by a number or a combination of numbers and letters. In 1933 a systematic method of designation was developed. So many different types have been introduced since that time that it has become impossible to always stick to the system that was set up.

The type number of a tube is divided into four parts. First, a number consisting of one or more digits designates the filament or heater voltage. Second, one or more letters designate the type or function of the tube. Third, a number designates the number of useful elements in the tube. Fourth, one or more letters designate the size or construction. For example, the type 2A3 is a power triode which requires a filament voltage of about 2 volts (actually 2.5 volts). It is an amplifier tube and has three useful elements. The fourth part of the designation is omitted. The type 5Y3-G is a duodiode which requires a filament voltage of 5 volts; it is a rectifier (letters from U to Z are used for rectifiers) and has three useful elements. The letter G indicates that the tube has a glass envelope. The type 50L6-GT requires a heater voltage of 50 volts, is a beam power amplifier (the letter L is used for such tubes) and has six useful elements if the heater and cathole are considered separately. The letters GT indicate the use of a glass envelope somewhat smaller than the conventional size.

Because of the thousands of different types of receiving tubes that have been manufactured, there are probably more exceptions to this system of designation than there are tubes which follow it completely.

For an explanation of the standard system for numbering base pins, refer to *Sockets for Tubes* in this chapter.

DATA AND USES OF THE TUBE MANUAL

Manufacturers of electron tubes have available listings of their particular tubes with the characteristics and technical descriptions. Several such publications do exist, known as tube manuals. The largest tube manuals (RCA, GE), which include several hundred pages or more, list only receiving-type electron tubes. When *tube manual* is referred to in this chapter, we mean the receiving tube manual. The appendix includes an excerpt from the 1948 *RCA*

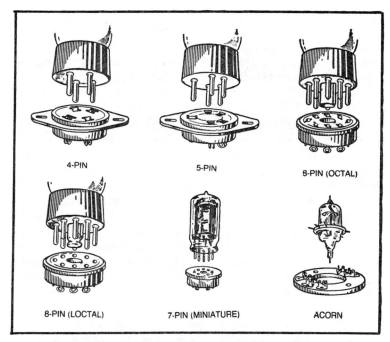

4-PIN   5-PIN   8-PIN (OCTAL)

8-PIN (LOCTAL)   7-PIN (MINIATURE)   ACORN

Fig. 1-18. Receiving-type electron-tube bases and corresponding sockets.

Receiving Tube Manual. This old edition, of course, is no longer in print.

Although no two of these tube manuals are identical, they all contain more or less the same type of information. Some older manuals were so designed that pages describing new tube types could be inserted to keep the books up-to-date. Now manuals are revised and reprinted from time to time.

The tubes are listed according to the numerical-alphabetical sequence of their type designations. The schematic symbol of each tube, showing the base-pin connections to the various electrodes, is given. A brief description of the tube is included in some manuals as an introduction to the tube characteristics. Next, the physical specifications are designated. These include information concerning the dimensions of the envelope, the type of base and sometimes the preferred mounting position.

Following the physical specification, the electrical ratings are given. These include information regarding the filament or heater voltage and current, as well as the maximum electrical ratings of the tube. Maximum plate and screen voltages, maximum plate and

31

screen dissipations, and peak heater-to-cathode voltage are included. In addition, the interelectrode capacitances of some types are listed. If the tube has other modes of operation—for example, a pentode operated as a triode or a pentode operated in push-pull—additional ratings and electrical specifications frequently are given.

Next, typical operation of the tube is shown. Figures for the following are often included: typical electrode voltages, required value of cathode bias resistor, peak signal voltage, typical electrode currents under conditions of zero and maximum signal, required value of load resistance, power output and total harmonic distortion. In addition, values of amplification factor, transconductance and plate resistance are supplied. If the tube commonly is operated under different conditions, a complete set of typical operating values frequently is included. For example, in one tube manual, maximum ratings and typical operating values are given for the 6L6 (beam power amplifier) under the following operating conditions: single-tube class A amplifier, single-tube class A amplifier (triode connected), push-pull class A amplifier, push-pull class AB$_1$ amplifier, and push-pull class AB$_2$ amplifier. Ratings also are given for most of the foregoing, using fixed bias or cathode bias.

Following the typical operating values is a section dealing with specific applications. Special installation notes having to do with the particular tube type also may be supplied, and unusual features of the tube are discussed.

Finally, one or more families of curves depicting the operation of the tubes are shown. Usually, these curves are the average plate characteristics for various values of grid voltage. Sometimes, one or more load lines are drawn on the characteristic curves. In some tube manuals, average transfer characteristic curves are shown, along with curves that illustrate the variation in plate resistance, transconductance and amplification factor at various electrode voltages.

If the particular tube listed happens to be a rectifier, ratings or curves are given which apply to use of the tube. The maximum peak inverse plate voltage and the maximum peak plate current are given, as well as the voltage drop across the tube at certain values of plate current. The output current for various AC input voltages and types of filter circuits is designated. Curves frequently are shown which give the DC output voltage and load current for various input voltages and filter circuits.

Many tube manuals supply additional information. A section dealing with general tube and circuit theory may be included. Sometimes the common tubes are classified as to their use and charac-

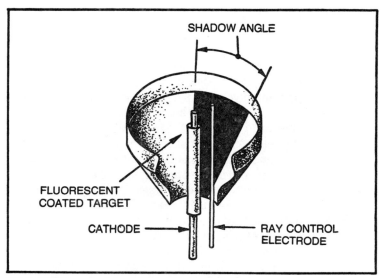

Fig. 1-19. Cutaway view of 6E5 electron-ray indicator.

teristics. Frequently, a section of the tube manual is devoted to the design of resistance-coupled voltage amplifiers. This section usually consists of tables for the commonly used amplifier tubes. The tables include information concerning the proper combination of plate load resistor, grid resistor, screen-grid resistor, cathode-bias resistor, and coupling and bypass capacitors for various values of plate-supply voltage. The output voltage, voltage gain and sometimes the percentage of distortion are also included under the various conditions outlined in the table.

Finally, the tube manual may contain circuit diagrams which illustrate some of the more important applications of the tubes listed in the manual. Some manuals provide information on obsolete or seldom encountered types, as well as on panel and ballast lamp specifications.

The tube manual provides a listing of the characteristics and socket connections of the electron tube. In servicing electronic equipment, it frequently is necessary to trace circuits, check components connected to various electrodes of tubes and measure tube electrode voltages. Because of the wide variety of electron tubes used in receivers and because of the general lack of standard base connections, it is often necessary to refer to a tube manual for socket connections. Remember that all views of tube bases or sockets are *bottom* views, unless otherwise indicated.

The normal operating voltages shown in the manual serve as a guide for servicing. You can compare the operating voltages given for a particular tube in the manual with the voltages measured in the equipment. If an electron tube is used for a special application, the operating voltages may not be similar to those shown in the manual. However, the measured voltages should not exceed the maximum ratings given and the filament or heater voltage should certainly correspond to the value designated in the manual.

The average plate characteristic curves have several uses. They show the operating conditions of the tube with various electrode potentials. These can be used to compare the actual operation of a tube in a circuit with the proper average operation. In addition, the curves serve as a basis for many useful calculations. A load line is constructed on the family of curves for the particular value of plate load used. By means of this load line and the curves shown in the manual, the power output and the percentage of distortion can be determined. These are determined by direct graphical methods; that is, actual values are read from the curves and these values are substituted in simple equation which show the power output and distortion. The curves are also used for design purposes. A given set of electrode potentials is assumed, a load line is drawn and calculations are based on the curves. These calculations show whether the plate dissipation of the tube is exceeded, and whether the power output and the fidelity are adequate. The transfer characteristic curve can be used to determine the operating range for tubes used for detection or for AVC action. Conversion characteristic curves are used in the design of converter stages, and diode load curves are useful in designing electron-tube voltmeters or AVC systems.

The tube manual permits a comparison between tubes. Comparative characteristics of several beam-power tubes, for example, can be examined to determine which tube fits the specific application required. In addition, physical dimensions of tubes can be found. This information is important in the mechanical design and construction of a piece of electronic equipment.

The section of the manual dealing with the design of resistance-coupled amplifiers gives specific component values that can be used to achieve certain results.

In addition to the preceding, some tube manuals contain an excellent section on theory and application of electron tubes. Illustrations frequently are included to show the internal construction of various types of receiving tubes.

ORIGIN OF RECEIVER INPUT

The purpose of a receiver is to convert the electromagnetic wave, from the transmitter, into energy usable by the human ear. Before entering into a discussion of the manner in which the receiver accomplishes this, you might find a brief review of the origination of the transmitted wave advantageous. Figure 1-20 illustrates the block diagram of a basic transmitter and the nature of the input and output energy of each section.

The input to the transmitter is in the form of sound waves, which are produced by voice, musical instruments, etc. These sound waves range in frequency from about 20 cycles per second (hertz) to about 20,000 cycles per second. The microphone converts the sound waves into an electrical signal which varies in frequency and amplitude in accordance with the original sound. Because the electrical signals from the microphone are very weak, they are fed to the modulating section (audio amplifier), which increases the amplitude to a level suitable as an input to the power amplifier.

In the rf unit, the power amplifier has two inputs. One input is the audio signal from the modulator, and the other is the constant amplitude radio frequency signal from the oscillator. In the broadcast band, the channel frequencies for various transmitters will range from 535 kHz to 1605 kHz. The output of the oscillator is called the *carrier* frequency. In the power amplifier, the audio signal (intelligence) is impressed on the carrier. The output of the power amplifier is a modulated rf signal, which is then fed to the antenna.

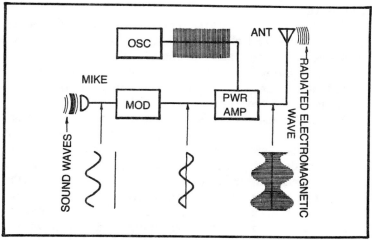

Fig. 1-20. Basic transmitter.

The antenna radiates the modulated rf signal in the form of electromagnetic waves. This electromagnetic wave will now be used as the input to the receiver.

FUNCTIONS OF A RECEIVER

A receiver must perform certain basic functions in order to be useful. In order of their performance, these functions are reception, selection, detection, af amplification and reproduction.

Reception involves having the transmitted electromagnetic wave pass through the receive antenna in such a manner as to induce a voltage in the antenna.

Selection involves being able to select a particular station's frequency from all the transmitted signals that happen to be induced in the receiving antenna at a given time.

Detection is the action of separating the low-frequency intelligence from the high-frequency carrier.

The *af amplification* involves amplifying the low-frequency intelligence (audio in the case of a radio) to the level required for operation of the reproducer.

Reproduction is the action of converting the electrical signals to sound waves which can then be interpreted by the ear as speech, music, or whatever.

The ability of a receiver to reproduce the signal of a very weak station is a function of the *sensitivity* of the receiver. In other words, the weaker a signal that can be applied to a receiver to still achieve the same value of signal output, the better is the sensitivity rating of that receiver.

The ability of a receiver to select and reproduce a desired signal from among several closely spaced stations, or from among interferring frequencies, is determined by the *selectivity* of the receiver. In other words, the better a receiver is at differentiating between desired and undesired signals, the better is the selectivity rating of the receiver.

Figure 1-21 shows the block diagram of a simple receiver that will perform all the functions required of a receiver. Also illustrated are the functions performed by the various sections of the receiver. The input to the receiver is the electromagnetic wave propagated from the antenna of the transmitter. This wave will pass through the antenna of the receiver and induce a small ac voltage. The section of the receiver formed by the antenna and L_1, perform the function of reception. L_1 is the primary of the input transformer, and the voltage induced in L_1 is coupled to the secondary, L_2. L_2 and C_1 form a tuned

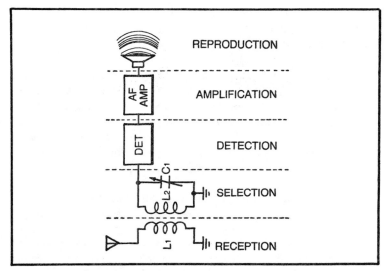

Fig. 1-21. Simple receiver block diagram.

circuit with C1 being variable to permit tuning across the broadcast band. Thus, the tuned input circuit performs the function of selecting a specific frequency from among those present in the antenna circuit. The output of the tuned circuit is a modulated rf signal.

This modulated rf signal is then fed to the detector circuit where the function of detection (rectification and filtering) is performed. The output of the detector circuit is a weak audio signal. The audio signal from the detector is too weak to satisfactorily operate a speaker; therefore, it is fed to an audio frequency amplifier to increase its amplitude. The output of the af amplifier is fed to the speaker, which performs the function of reproduction—converting the electrical signals back to the form of the original input to the transmitter. (In this case, we're referring to sound waves).

DIODE DETECTOR

The first widely used receiver, the crystal set of fond memory, was exceeding simple, yet it had all of the functions depicted in Fig. 1-21 save amplification. Its circuit diagram is shown in Fig. 1-22. There's something strangely fascinating and appealing about a device that is so simple and yet can pull sounds out of the air that originated many miles away.

The crystal detector was invented in 1906 by two Americans, H.H. Dunwoody and G.W. Pickard. The crystal was a hunk of quartz or galena. One connection was made to the base of the crystal, the other crystal connection was made to a sensitive spot —which one found by trial and error—by means of a short and very fine wire, which was called a *cat's whisker*.

Up until about 1920, most radio receivers were homemade crystal sets. Crystal sets were manufactured as home-entertainment instruments for several years thereafter. In 1922, such a set sold for about $25. Eventually they were replaced in the home-entertainment market by tube-type radios, but they were made as toys for quite a number of years longer. In fact, the construction of crystal sets is still an attractive divertisement for experimenters.

The function of a radio receiver is to intercept a small percentage of the radio-wave energy radiated from the antennas of transmitters and recover the original intelligence contained in it.

The transmitter of a radio station may have an output power on the order of thousands of watts, and the voltage on the transmitting antenna may be on the order of thousands of volts. However, the value of rf energy intercepted by the receiver depends on many factors: the distance between the transmitter and the receiver, the location of the receiver (in a valley, on a hill, behind a building, etc.), the type of receiving antenna used (directional, high gain, etc.), orientation of the receiver antenna, the power of the transmitter, and the type of terrain over which the signal passes on its way to the receiver. Therefore, after taking all of these factors into consideration, it is not surprising to find that usually the receiving antenna intercepts only a few *microwatts* of power, and the voltage induced in the antenna is measured in *microvolts*.

In Fig. 1-22 the antenna performs the function of reception. Selection of the desired signal is accomplished by adjusting the variable tuning coil, L_1. The crystal detector (CR_1) rectifies the signal, and the capacitor (C_1) filters the rf component of the detected signal. The audio component of the signal is then passed on to the earphones, which perform the function of reproduction by converting the electrical signal into sound waves. Later, the crystal was sometimes replaced by a vacuum-tube diode.

It was difficult for a family to enjoy a radio broadcast when only one person at a time could use the earphones. This problem led, by popular demand, to another function being added to the receiver—audio amplification. Now the set produced enough power to operate a speaker, and everybody could hear the reproduced sound waves at the same time. Reception was still difficult, and as the broadcast

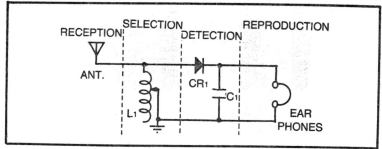

Fig. 1-22. Crystal set schematic.

spectrum began to fill up with stations, it became increasingly more difficult to separate one station from the other. It was discovered that the addition of rf amplifier stages not only increased the sensitivity of the set (allowed reception of weaker stations), but also its selectivity (allowed better discrimination between adjacent stations).

In the search for improved reception, engineers added 3, 4 and sometimes 6 stages of tuned radio frequency amplification to the receivers. This led to increased problems in tuning and neutralization.

Many of the problems of the trf receivers were reduced or eliminated by the introduction of the superheterodyne principle of reception, and today practically all radio receivers use this principle. The tuned rf amplifier is not necessary to the operation of a superheterodyne receiver, but one or more rf amplifiers are included in higher quality receivers where better reception is desired.

All electron tubes have the characteristic of unilateral conductivity. Consequently, any one of them can serve as a rectifying device. Combined with a filter, a triode—for example—can serve as a detector in the same manner as the diode detector.

Having no grid, a diode cannot amplify a signal. As a matter of fact, the output taken from a diode stage is less than its input. This disadvantage is overcome by using a tube with a grid, such as a triode or pentode. The signal is not only detected, but is also amplified in one stage. In early receivers, this arrangement was necessary because of the lack of rf amplification. As much gain as possible had to be achieved.

The operation of the grid-leak triode detector (Fig. 1-23) is as follows: the signal voltage applied to the grid of the triode tube is alternately positive and negative; grid current flows during the half cycles in which the grid is positive with relation to the cathode;

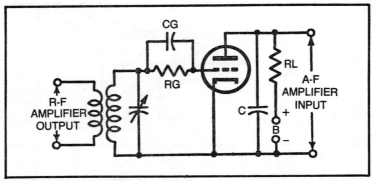

Fig. 1-23. Circuit of grid-leak detector.

during the negative half cycles, no grid current flows; as a result, a unidirectional pulsating direct current flows through Rg. Capacitor Cg serves as a filter to smooth the rf pulses. A DC voltage is produced across Rg, and this voltage varies at an audio rate just as in the case of the diode detector.

The af voltage across the grid resistor now can be used as a signal voltage for the triode amplifier. As a result, an amplified af signal appears in the plate circuit of the grid-lead detector. Capacitor C is an additional rf filter.

The grid-leak detector operates as a *square-law* device. A square-law detector is one whose af output voltage varies as the square of the rf input voltage. In the diode detector, by comparison, the output varies directly with the input.

The development of higher-gain rf amplifiers led to the replacement of the grid-lead detector by the half-wave diode detector. The diode detector distorts the af signal much less than the grid-leak detector.

In 1912, the American inventor Edward Howard Armstrong conceived the notion of taking part of the rf output of the triode and feeding it back to the input for further amplification. The enhanced input, in turn resulted in a much stronger output than was obtainable with an ordinary triode detector. Because of its simplicity, sensitivity and selectivity, the feedback or regenerative detector of Armstrong was popular with experimenters for many years. When radio manufacturing began in earnest in about 1920, the regenerative circuit was at the height of its popularity. A few years later, it was suceeded as the sensation of the radio world by the *neutrodyne* receiver. In 1922, a one-tube regenerative set sold for about $80.

The regenerative circuit is mainly of historic interest. It is little used anymore, though it is still the most sensitive circuit possible with a triode. The regenerative detector was the first important use of the triode. Between the invention of the triode by DeForest in 1906 and the invention of the feedback circuit in 1912, the application of the triode had been in limbo. Some nonfeedback triode detectors had been built, but they offered little improvement over other detectors. The regenerative principle was later to prove important to transmitters as well as receivers. In fact, the regenerative oscillator is the basis of the transmitters used today.

When high sensitivity and selectivity are the most important factors to be considered, a regenerative detector may be used. However, the linearity as well as the ability to handle strong signals without overloading is very poor.

A grid-leak detector may be modified to operate as a regenerative detector, as indicated in Fig. 1-24. Because an amplified rf component is present in the plate circuit of the grid-leak detector, regeneration can be obtained by connecting a coil (L2), known as a *tickler coil*, in series with the plate circuit so that it is inductively coupled to the grid coil (L3).

With an rf signal across L3, an rf component of plate current flows through L2. L2 is connected so that the voltage it induces in L3 is in phase with the incoming signal voltage applied to the grid. Thus, the voltage gain of the stage is increased.

It is important that the voltage fed back by the tickler coil be in phase with the incoming signal voltage. Otherwise the feedback will be degenerative and the amplification will be reduced. Furthermore, if the coupling between L2 and L3 is too great, oscillation will take place. For receiving code signals, oscillation is desirable in order to produce an audible beat tone. However, it is not desirable for voice or music reception because of the objectionable squeal from the beat tone. The regenerative detector is the most sensitive triode detec-

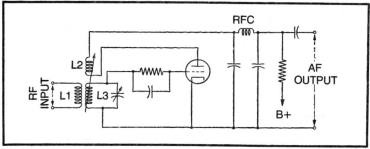

Fig. 1-24. Regenerative detector.

tor circuit possible when it is operated just below the point of oscillation.

TRF RECEIVER

The tuned radio frequency receiver, generally known as the trf receiver, consists of one or more rf stages, a detector stage, one or more af stages, a reproducer and the necessary power supply. A block diagram of a trf receiver is shown in Fig. 1-25. The waveforms that appear in the respective sections of the receiver are shown above the block diagram.

The amplitude of the AM signal at the input of the receiver is relatively small because it has been attenuated in the space between the transmitter and the receiver. It is composed of the carrier frequency and two sideband frequencies. The rf amplifier stages amplify the waveform, but they do not change its basic shape if the circuits are operating properly. The detector rectifies and removes the rf component of the signal. The output of the detector is a weak signal made up only of the modulation component, of the incoming signal. The af amplifier stages following the detector increase the amplitude of the af signal to a value sufficient to operate the loudspeaker or earphones.

The plain trf receiver was popular with experimenters in the early days, and with manufacturers throughout the 1920s. It was gradually replaced by the neutrodyne and superheterodyne circuits. One of the problems with trf receivers was a tendency of the rf stages to break into oscillation when operated at high gain. As in Armstrong's detector, the regeneration was intentional and controlled so it could be kept below the point of oscillation. In trf receivers, the regeneration was unintentional and occurred within the triode itself. At first, the only way to control it was to limit the amount of amplification in each stage and to use several stages.

In 1922 the *neutrodyne* receiver became popular. This was a trf set with additonal circuitry, invented by L. Alan Hazeltine, that counteracted the self-oscillation tendency of the triode rf amplifier. Neutrodynes were still popular in the mid-1930's. The neutrodyne was the most popular of all radio sets until the superheterodyne came along to gradually replace it. It offered a high-performance, low-cost alternative to the $250 trf sets then on the market.

SUPERHETERODYNE RECEIVERS

The superheterodyne (or superhet) receiver was invented by Edwin Howard Armstrong in 1918. It was introduced by RCA in

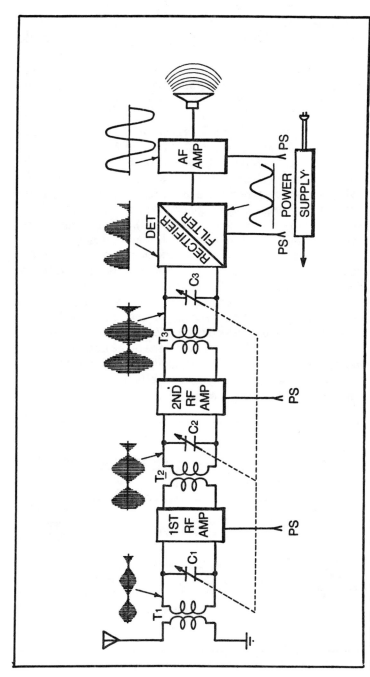

Fig. 1-25. Block diagram of a trf receiver and waveforms.

1924 and has been the standard receiver ever since. In 1927, Westinghouse manufactured a superhet that could be plugged into ordinary electrical outlets (which were often 32 volts), eliminating batteries. Between 1924 and 1927, RCA kept the superhet circuit to itself, but by 1927 the radio market was too enormous for even a few giants to hold, so RCA began to license the superheterodyne to many other companies. How radio grew up in the Roaring Twenties is evidenced by the growth of RCA sales: from $1 million in 1921 to $11 million in 1922 to $51 million in 1924 to $87 million in 1928.

The essential difference between the trf receiver and the superheterodyne receiver is that in the former, the rf amplifiers preceding the detector are tunable over a band of frequencies and in the latter, the corresponding amplifiers are tuned to one fixed frequency, called the *intermediate frequency* (i-f). The principle of frequency conversion by heterodyne action is here employed to convert any desired station frequency within the receiver range to this intermediate frequency. Thus, an incoming signal is converted to the fixed intermediate frequency before detecting the audio signal component, and the i-f amplifier operates under uniformly optimum conditions throughout the receiver range. The i-f circuits thus may be made to have uniform selectivity, uniform high voltage gain, and uniform satisfactory bandwidth to contain all of the desired sideband components associated with the amplitude-modulated carrier.

The block diagram of a typical superheterodyne receiver is shown in Fig. 1-26. Below corresponding sections of the receiver

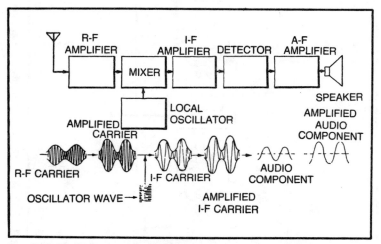

Fig. 1-26. Block diagram of a superheterodyne receiver and waveforms.

are shown the waveforms of the signal at that point. The rf signal from the antenna passes first through an rf amplifier (preselector) where the amplitude of the signal is increased. A locally generated unmodulated rf signal of constant amplitude is then mixed with the carrier frequency in the mixer stage. The mixing or heterodyning of these two frequencies produces an intermediate-frequency signal that contains all of the modulation characteristics of the original signal. The intermediate frequency is equal to the difference between the station frequency and the oscillator frequency associated with the heterodyne mixer. The intermediate frequency is then amplified in one or more stages called *intermediate-frequency* (i-f) amplifiers and fed to a conventional detector for recovery of the audio signal.

The detector signal is amplified in the af section and then fed to a headset or loudspeaker. The detector, the af section, and the reproducer of a superheterodyne receiver are basically the same as those in a trf set.

Chapter 2
Understanding Schematics

A picture is worth a thousand words. Man has used pictures as a means of communications for many years. If an engineer designed a simple electronic device, for example, it would be difficult to convey his idea to the person who is to fabricate the object without a drawing to show the shape, size and location of the components. Drawings are used not only as plans to fabricate and assemble objects; they are also used to show how to service most products, including radio sets.

The three types of drawings most used in servicing radios are the pictorial drawing, the wiring diagram and the schematic.

A pictorial drawing is a drawing that takes the place of a photograph. It shows the shape, location and relative size of objects. One such drawing is the one in Fig. 2-1, which shows a circuit mounted on the back of a military radio receiver. Another example of a pictorial drawing, one very useful to a restorer of antique radios, is a drawing showing how the dial cord of a receiver is to be strung.

A wiring diagram is more abstract (less like a photograph) than a pictorial. It also shows the shape, size and locations of components, but the person drawing it takes some liberties. He shows the same parts, but in less detail. Furthermore, he usually shows the wires as being as straight as a string, which usually they aren't. Figure 2-2 is a wiring diagram of the same circuit shown in Fig. 2-1.

The schematic represents a still higher level of abstraction. It is not at all like a photograph. It uses symbols to represent electronic

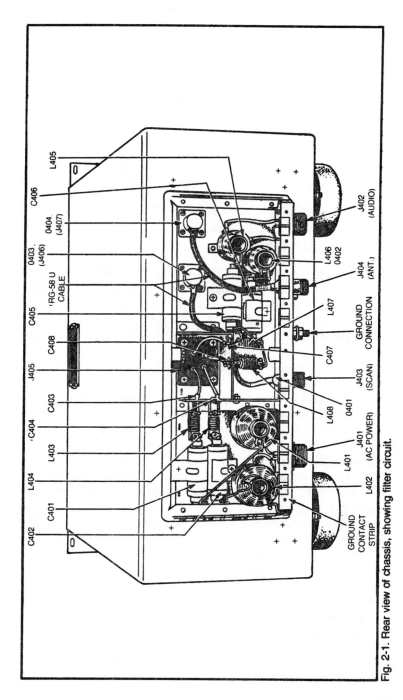

Fig. 2-1. Rear view of chassis, showing filter circuit.

47

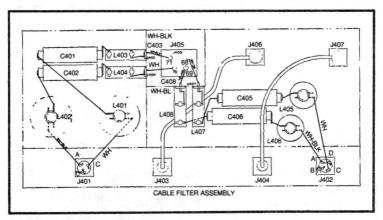

Fig. 2-2. Filter wiring diagram.

parts, and the shape and size of the symbols bear little or no relation to the shape or size of the parts represented. Further, the locations of the symbols often do not reflect the actual placement of the parts in the actual circuit. Usually the symbols are arranged so that the input is placed at the upper left corner, and the signals and action flow from left to right and from top to bottom. Figure 2-3 shows the schematic of the same circuit depicted in Figs. 2-1 and 2-2.

Service literature for the old-time sets is difficult to come by since these sets are often "orphans"—that is, their manufacturers are out of business. There were a number of books of service information put out by independent publishing companies that covered the old sets. The most complete is *Rider's Perpetual Trouble Shooter Manuals*, which cover the era from 1930 to 1953. Some libraries in medium-size and large cities have complete sets of Rider's manuals. The information in these runs from a one-page schematic for some sets to 19 pages for one Scott model. There are a number of persons selling copies of schematics and other information from these books. They charge from 25 cents per page to $3.50 for all the information available for a given model. For the names and addresses of the providers of this service, look in the classified section of *Elementary Electronics, Popular Electronics* and *Radio-Electronics*.

Gernsback also published a set of *Official Radio Service Manuals* back in the 1930s (1930-1937). These will also prove very helpful, if you can find them.

One long-time supplier of service information is still in business, and that is Supreme Publications, (P.O. Box 46, Highland Park, IL

48

60035). They supply volumes covering numerous models and also information on specific individual models.

For other sources of servicing information and general information about old-time radio—and for just plain fun reading—I highly recommend *Elementary Electronics'* monthly "Antique Radio Corner," which is presided over by James A. Fred.

To understand schematics, it is necessary to understand the symbols used in them. The following pages show pictorial drawings of the most common radio parts and the schematic symbols for the parts. First we shall consider the unit terms used in electricity and electronics, and on schematics.

UNIT TERMS USED IN ELECTRICITY

A review of the unit terms in electricity is given in this section of the chapter. It is essential that the radio restorer have a thorough understanding of these terms so that he can properly (and easily) interpret schematic diagrams, block diagrams, and service block diagrams. The more knowledge you have of electronic theories, the easier it will be for you to read electronic diagrams and schematics. (If you plan to become professionally involved in receiver restora-

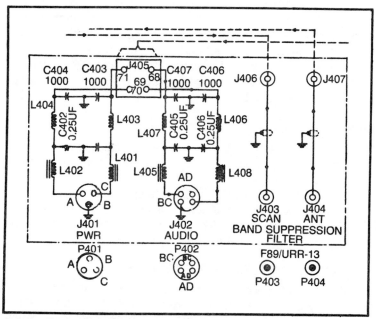

Fig. 2-3. Filter schematic.

tion, or deeply involved as an amateur, it will pay you to study the advanced receiver theory, given in the appendix.)

Coulombs

Man has never seen an electron and maybe never will. To simplify the job of counting them, individual electrons are grouped together into a large electronic unit—the coulomb—much like grouping grains of sugar into a larger unit, such as the pound.

Amperes

When 1 coulomb of electricity passes a point in 1 second, 1 ampere of electricity is flowing. Thus, 1 ampere is to electrical flow as 1 gallon-per-minute is to water flow. In other words, we are dealing with the rate of flow. One-half coulomb per second is ½ ampere; 1/1000 coulomb per second is 1/1000 ampere, or 1 milliampere (abbreviated mA).

In radio work, the most used unit of current is the milliampere. With receiving circuits, the range is from 1 or 2 to about 50 mA.

Volts

Volume of current is not always the same. It varies directly with the size of the charge. Work is required to move electrons and create a charge. Consequently, the size of the charge may be expressed in units of work necessary to move the charge.

The volt is the unit used to express the amount of work done to create a charge. One volt of charge is created when 1 joule of work is expended in moving 1 coulomb.

Joules

The joule is the term used to express the absolute unit of work or energy applied. In this application, 1 joule is equal to approximately 0.7375 foot-pound.

A volt, however, actually expresses more than the degree of charge. When you accumulate a surplus of electrons, a reverse of potential energy is created. Thus, 1 volt may also be used as an expression of the potential energy of an object.

VOLTAGES ARE DIFFERENCES IN POTENTIALS

Because it is possible to create an electrical charge by either adding or removing electrons, the energy of two points is not expressed in actual potentials but in differences of potential. When you say an object has a potential of 200 volts, you actually are expressing the difference in the potentials of two points.

Zero Potential

All objects have some potential, but it is common practice to designate some point as zero potential. In a radio, zero potential is usually the frame or chassis of the set. When you say the plate of a vacuum tube is positive 200 volts, you are only stating that the plate is 200 volts more positive than is the chassis.

The rate of current flow is influenced by the magnitude of the difference between the two charges. If the difference between the charges is small, for example, the rate of flow will be low. If the difference is large, the rate of flow will be large.

Negative Potentials

Negative potentials also exist. Although the chassis of a radio is given as zero potential, it is possible for certain parts of a receiver to be at a lower potential than is the chassis. These parts are said to have negative potentials.

You will find the grids of vacuum tubes rated as −5, −10, −50, or −75 volts. This expression means that the grids of the tubes are at a lower positive potential than the chassis by 5, 10, 50, or 75 volts. Don't let a negative potential fool you. There is just as much wallop between −200 volts and the chassis as between +200 volts and the chassis.

Voltages Are Relative

Voltages are relative. Point A in Fig. 2-4 is given as −200 volts in comparison to the chassis. Point B, on the other hand, is 200 volts more positive than is the chassis. You may say, therefore, that point B is 400 volts more positive than point A. Reversing the expression, point A is 400 volts negative in respect to B.

How about point C? It is 100 volts positive in respect to the chassis, but 100 volts more negative than point B. In respect to A, point C is 300 volts positive.

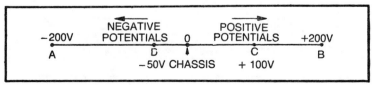

Fig. 2-4. Relative potentials.

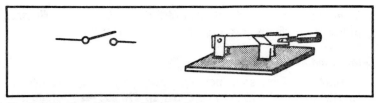

Fig. 2-5. Single-pole, single-throw switch.

Point D is 50 volts negative in respect to the chassis, but 150 volts positive in respect to point A. Thus, point D is also 150 volts more negative than C, and 250 volts more negative than B.

All these potentials (voltages) are measured in relation to the potential of the chassis. When you state the voltage of an element, therefore, remember that what you state is true only in respect to, or relative to, another point.

Here is a little statement to remember: electrons flow toward the more positive potential. Even if all potentials are negative the electrons move from the most negative toward the least negative potential. The higher the voltage and the greater the potential difference, the greater is the flow of electrons.

INFLUENCING FACTORS

Now that we have covered the essentials of electricity, we will move into the components, their influencing factors, and their symbols. In drawing electronic schematics it would be difficult and time-consuming to represent each component as an actual picture. Instead, standard symbols are used to represent parts and components. The symbols are universal and are readily understood throughout the world.

Before you try to interpret electronic schematics and diagrams, you should become familiar with some of the electronic symbols and their influencing factors on the circuit. A few of the more common electrical and electronic symbols are explained in the following paragraphs and are illustrated as cited.

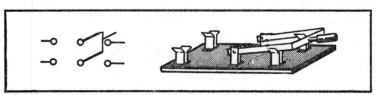

Fig. 2-6. Double-pole, double-throw switch.

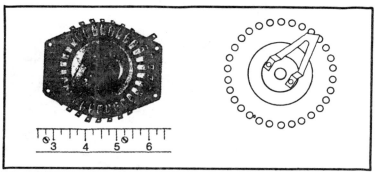

Fig. 2-7. Wafer switch.

Switches

A simple single-pole, single-throw knife switch is shown in Fig. 2-5. It makes and breaks a connection for one line, and only at one point. The symbol shows two small circles indicating contact points and a straight line indicating the movable throw switch.

Figure 2-6 illustrates a double-pole, double-throw switch. It is similar to the single-throw switch, except that it has two blade switches mechanically connected, and can make and break contact in two different positions.

A wafer switch is shown in Fig. 2-7. The symbol indicates a 3-pole, 3-circuit switch with two nonshorting and one shorting moving contact.

Two types of fuses are illustrated in Fig. 2-8. There are many types of fuses but they all have the same function: to protect a circuit from overloading. The two types of fuses shown are the cartridge type and the screw-in type. When a circuit draws too much current, a metal wire or strip within the fuse melts, interrupting the flow of current. Note that the symbol is the same regardless of fuse type.

Resistors

One of the most common electronic components is the resistor. A resistor opposes the flow of electrons. Thus far, only the voltage

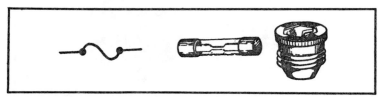

Fig. 2-8. Fuses.

53

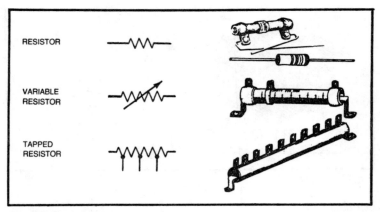

Fig. 2-9. Resistors.

has been given as a factor influencing the rate of flow of electrons. In some substances, such as glass, rubber and cotton, resistance is great enough to stop the flow completely. Three types of resistors and their symbols are illustrated in Fig. 2-9.

Figure 2-10 illustrates the potentiometer and its symbol. A potentiometer is a variable resistor commonly used as a volume control for radios and television sets.

A rheostat and its symbol are shown in Fig. 2-11. A rheostat is another form of a variable resistor. It is similar in construction to a potentiometer. A rheostat is almost always wirewound, whereas a potentiometer can be either of wire or carbon.

Capacitors

Three types of capacitors and their symbols are illustrated in Fig. 2-12. Capacitors are devices used to store or release electrons as they are needed in the circuit.

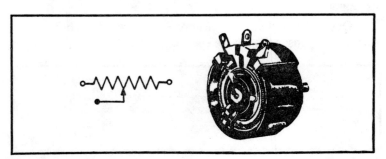

Fig. 2-10. Potentiometer.

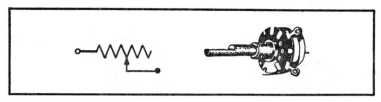

Fig. 2-11. Rheostat.

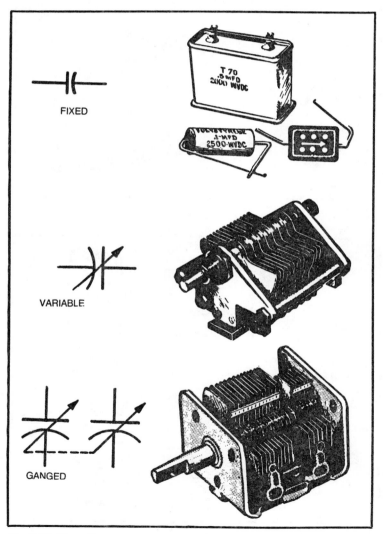

FIXED

VARIABLE

GANGED

Fig. 2-12. Capacitors.

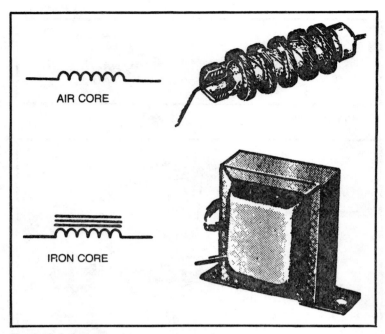

AIR CORE

IRON CORE

Fig. 2-13. Inductors.

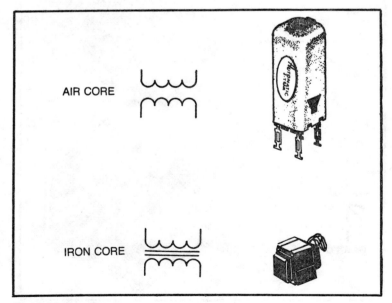

AIR CORE

IRON CORE

Fig. 2-14. Transformers.

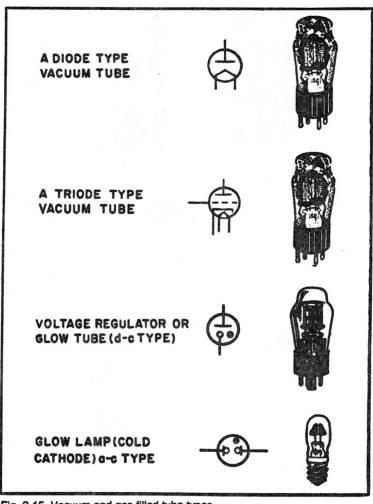

Fig. 2-15. Vacuum and gas-filled tube types.

Types of Coils

Figure 2-13 illustrates two types of inductors and their symbols. One is an air-core, coil type, and the other is an iron core, usually referred to as a *choke*. Inductors are used to smooth out variations in current flow.

Two types of transformers and their symbols are shown in Fig. 2-14. Transformers are used to step AC voltage up or down, or to transfer AC voltage from the primary to the secondary.

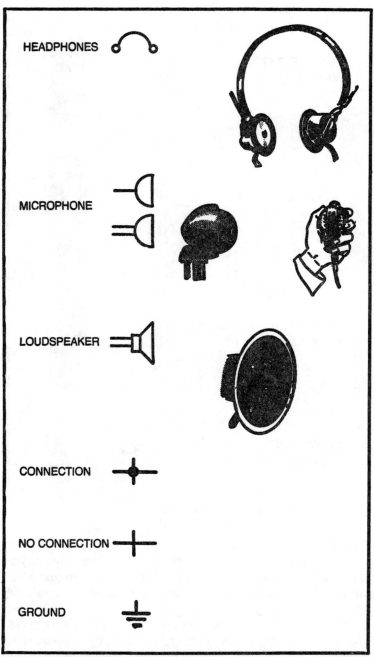

HEADPHONES

MICROPHONE

LOUDSPEAKER

CONNECTION

NO CONNECTION

GROUND

Fig. 2-16. Symbols and illustrations of ground, wire connections and some common radio accessories.

Four of the many types of tubes are seen in Fig. 2-15. Symbols with black dots within the circle indicate that the tube is gas-filled. Other symbols have no black dots within the circle and indicate that the tube is a vacuum tube.

Figure 2-16 illustrates the symbols used for ground and wire connections. You are no doubt familiar with headphones, microphones, loudspeakers, wires and ground connections; they need no explanation.

Chapter 3
Start Here!

This chapter will tell you how to locate and repair a failure of an antique radio as quickly and easily as possible. It will tell you how to check other parts and circuits for damage or indications of possible failure, so that once a set is fixed, it will stay fixed for a while.

The cut-and-try method, or haphazard checking, such as testing the antenna circuit, then the audio circuit, then the i-f stages, and so on, wastes time. Certain circuits and components may be missed, and a thorough job cannot be done. The service procedure described next is a logical method of servicing old-time radio sets. By following the procedure, troubles will be located faster, and circuit components will not be overlooked.

A TROUBLESHOOTING METHOD THAT NEVER FAILS

The first operation in overhauling and repairing a set is to thoroughly inspect and clean the set. To accomplish this quickly and avoid any oversights, the operation is divided into the following seven steps. Then preliminary troubleshooting, trouble localization, and trouble isolation follow.

Cleaning and Inspecting Procedure

- **Removing Plug-In Parts.** Remove all plug-in parts, such as tubes, crystals, pilot lamps, and other parts that can be removed without unsoldering wires. Octal tubes can usually be removed from the sockets by merely pulling up on the part in question. In some units, tubes and vibrators are held in place with clamps. To avoid damage to components, release the tension bar on the clamp before attempting to remove the tube or vibrator. Loctal type tubes should be rocked slightly to one side until a click is heard. Then the tube can be lifted out of the socket. Some parts have their leads soldered to a removable terminal strip. These parts should also be removed after loosening the terminal-strip lockscrews, or nuts. Some radio sets have plug-in type rf or i-f coils which can be removed by loosening the lockscrews holding the shield cans to the chassis.

- **Cleaning Set.** After loose dirt has been blown from the radio, use a rag soaked in a solvent to clean each part thoroughly, removing any dirt or grease. Be sure, when cleaning the parts, that the wiring is not disturbed; otherwise, when the radio is reassembled and ready to operate, oscillation, degeneration, voltage breakdown, arcover, or distortion may result. As Fig. 3-1 shows, the old sets had many parts on the chassis, but they were not as tightly packed as parts in modern sets. If it is necessary to move wiring, be sure it is returned to its original position.

Dirt or corrosion that has accumulated on contacts and sockets can cause operating problems. Dirt on the chassis can also hide

Fig. 3-1. Bottom view of the sparsely populated chassis of the Sparton Model 1281.

Fig. 3-2. This filter capacitor was leaky in a literal sense, as the chassis corrosion shows.

defects such as the leaky electrolytic capacitor in Fig. 3-2. Remove any dirt or corrosion that has accumulated on contacts with solvent and sandpaper.

Corrosion is a common problem in old sets. The amount of corrosion on the chassis in Fig. 3-3 and the stations selected on the push-button tuner suggested that the radio in question, an old Sparton console, had spent quite a bit of time at the seashore. In a case like this, corrosion of mechanical parts is likely. Remove all corrosion and gum from tuning capacitor shafts, tuning capacitors, and any other mechanical parts in the set.

- **Visual and Mechanical Inspection.** After cleaning the unit, make a thorough examination of all parts and wiring cables, noting the need for replacing any parts found defective. Locating and replacing slightly damaged parts at this time will help to prevent failure of the equipment at some future date. Some of the parts which should be checked are socket contacts, contact springs, gears, tuning capacitors, volume controls, band switches, insulators, sockets for plug-in parts, terminal strips, jacks, loose bolts, rivets, catches, snaps, hinges and nuts. In many instances, noise and intermittent operation are caused by one or more of these defects. In addition to the visual inspection, all operating controls and moveable parts should be inspected for wear and correct operation. Turn each operating control clockwise as far as it will go, then counterclockwise as far as it will go. If binding occurs in either direction, make a note to correct the condition. Any appreciable amount of backlash in tuning-control gear assemblies should also be noted. Troubles of this nature usually require the replacement of a shaft, bushing, or gear assembly and should be corrected as soon as electrical checks have been completed.

- **Determining Cause of Part Damage.** After inspecting the equipment for defective parts, you might find that a capacitor has been shorted, or a resistor burned up, or the insulation on wires burned. In each case, it will be necessary to determine the cause of these failures, since replacing the part may not clear up the trouble but burn up the new part. *Only after the cause of trouble has been determined should a new part be installed.*
- **Replacing Defective Parts.** When replacing defective parts, be sure that the new parts used are placed in the same position as the part that was removed. If wires were moved, be sure that the wires are returned to the original position; otherwise, the equipment may not operate correctly. Also replace all parts that were noted as defective in the earlier step outlining visual and mechanical inspection.
- **Lubrication.** Practically all mechanical moving parts used in radio sets require some form of lubrication. After the parts have been cleaned and inspected, lubricate them with a suitable oil or grease (Fig. 3-4). Mechanical parts, such as bearings on tuning capacitors, gears, shafts, springs and

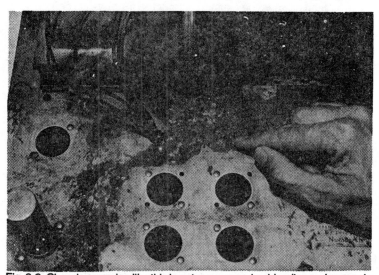

Fig. 3-3. Chassis corrosion like this is not uncommon in old radios and suggests the desirability of checking plugs, prongs, contacts and mechanical parts for corrosion. The chassis shown was apparently affected by the salt air of the seashore.

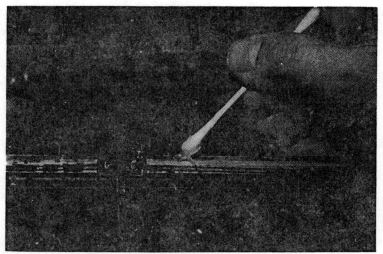

Fig. 3-4. After cleaning, lubricate the parts.

pivot points, cause noise, improper tuning and intermittent operation of the equipment unless properly lubricated.

• **Cleaning, Inspecting and Testing Plug-In Parts.** The plug-in parts, which were removed before the unit was cleaned, must be cleaned, inspected for physical defects and tested for electrical performance before they are reinstalled in the unit. Dirt and grease on the tube prongs can be removed with a solvent. After this is done, it is recommended that fine sandpaper be used to remove any dirt or corrosion that still exists. This is *very important*, since the dirt or corrosion that occurs on the tube prongs will cause a high-resistance connection between the tube prongs and the socket contact. After cleaning, check the tubes in a tube checker and replace any found defective. Be sure that cable plugs have clean prongs, and that the cables are not frayed (see Fig. 3-5). An ohmmeter can be used to check cording continuity. Wiggling the cord at the socket or plug will often reveal intermittent shorts or loose connections. Make sure that all plugs fit snugly into their sockets.

PRELIMINARY TROUBLESHOOTING

A logical procedure should be followed in repairing even the simplest piece of equipment. A few preliminary tests often locate the source of trouble without extensive testing with instruments.

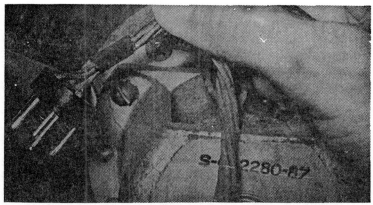

Fig. 3-5. Check the cable plugs for clean prongs and cables that are not frayed.

The senses of smell, sight, hearing and touch often localize the source of trouble quickly. After the unit is in operation a few minutes, it may be possible to note unusual odors, such as sealing compound, indicating an overloaded transformer (Fig. 3-6); burning paint, usually indicating an overheated resistor; and burning rubber, probably indicating defective insulation. If any unusual odor is detected coming from a part, the trouble may be in that part, or in its associated circuit. Look for smoking parts and sparking. Look for

Fig. 3-6. After warm-up, unusual odors indicate an overheated transformer.

any wax-impregnated paper capacitors that are surrounded by a pool of melted paraffin, usually indicative of a defective capacitor. Hum, scratch noises, and other odd sounds should have a special meaning to the repairman. In general, certain sounds indicate certain types of trouble. For example, hum can indicate a shorted or open filter capacitor. Scratchy noises, heard when the tuning control is moved, can indicate dirty rotor contacts, or foreign particles caught on the plates of the tuning capacitor. In most cases, touching the tubes after the unit has been turned on for a few minutes will show whether or not the filaments are heated. If a tube remains cold, the filament of the tube is burned out, or is not getting filament voltage. After the unit has been turned on for a time, turn it off and cautiously touch the different parts, such as resistors, transformers, and capacitors. Notice if these parts are overheated.

CAUTION To prevent shock, capacitors in high-voltage circuits (such as used in power supplies) should be discharged by placing a low-value resistor across the capacitor after turning off the power.

Finding the Bad Stage

Localization means tracing the trouble to a stage of a section. Before removing the chassis from the cabinet, and prior to disconnecting cables, be sure that power is being supplied, the tubes are not at fault, the antenna is intact and connected and that the defect is not something that can be corrected without disassembling the equipment. For example, if a receiver is completely inoperative, turn the sensitivity and the audio gain controls up to produce maximum output. If only noise is heard, the local oscillator rf stage, or the mixer stage is defective. Check the tubes in these stages. The following tests are used in tracking down trouble:

- After the chassis has been removed from the cabinet, check the resistance at the point where the DC from the power supply is applied to the stages, to tell whether there is a short circuit in the power supply.

- Find out which portion of the equipment (rf, i-f, or audio) is faulty. Use signal substitution which is discussed shortly.

Note that localizing the trouble to a subchassis or to a portion of the main chassis is also referred to as **sectionalization.**

- Check the suspected tubes with a tube tester or by substitution.

- Make voltage measurements in the plate, screen-grid and bias lines and at the tube sockets of the suspected stages.

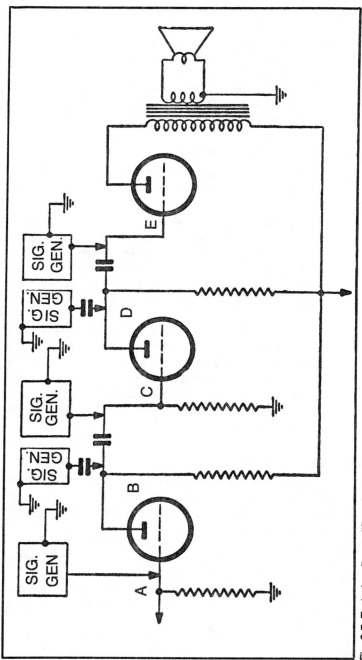

Fig. 3-7. Typical audio amplifier, showing signal-substitution points.

- Measure resistances at the points where the voltages are abnormal.
- If the complaint is a weak receiver, and other tests fail to detect the troublesome stage, stage-gain measurements must be made. This means feeding a signal of a given strength into the suspected stages and measuring the strength of the signal at the output of those stages and comparing it with that of a good set.

Finding the Bad Tube or Other Part

Isolation means tracing the trouble to a part, such as a capacitor, resistor, transformer, or relay. Isolation is usually done by:

— Using the senses as was instructed in the sections on sectionalization and localization, but in this case it may lead the repairman directly to the defective part.
— Making voltage and resistance measurements at the tube sockets. Examples of this are covered in Chapter 4.
— Signal substitution and signal tracing as used in localization.
— If a tube is defective, it probably will be located in localization. However, there may be a component part that has short-circuited and, at the same time, has damaged a tube.
— Stage-gain tests may not be necessary at this point, but if they are, the information in localization applies.
— Bridging the suspected part, such as a capacitor, with one known to be good.

SIGNAL SUBSTITUTION

If a receiver is completely inoperative, or one is weak and does not improve when aligned, the trouble can be quickly localized to a stage by **signal tracing,** or **signal substitution.** If the receiver is completely inoperative, the signal-substitution method produces quickest results and requires only a signal generator and a set of headphones for testing. This method may not locate the actual defect, but it will indicate the defective stage.

Inject an af (audio frequency) signal into the grid of the audio-output stage, at E in Fig. 3-7, and note if the stage will pass a signal, which should be heard in the speaker. If it does, move the audiogenerator connection from E to D, then to C, B, and A. Work back to the detector, determining if each stage will pass and amplify

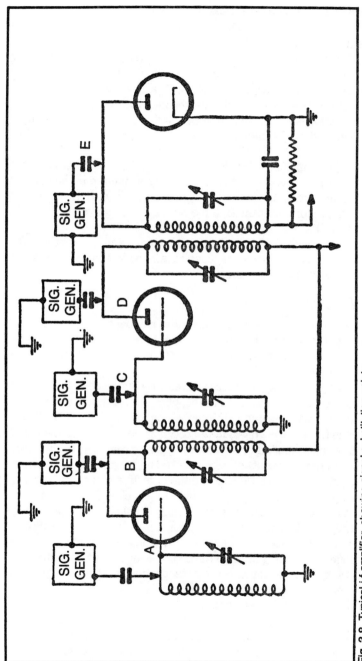

Fig. 3-8. Typical i-f amplifier, showing signal-substitution points.

the signal. Use a 0.01-pF capacitor in series with the lead to the af signal source. If the af stages pass and amplify the signal, check the i-f stages.

Inject a modulated i-f signal of the correct frequency into the grid or diode plate of the detector, as shown at Fig. 3-8E and then into the i-f stages, as shown at D, C, B, and A, working back to the plate of the mixer and listening for the modulating tone in a headset. Use a 0.001-ωF capacitor in series with the lead to the i-f signal source. If the i-f stages pass the signal, check the mixer and r-f stages (if any).

Inject a modulated rf signal into the grid of the mixer stage, as shown at E in Fig. 3-9 and note if the signal is heard in the headset when the set is tuned to the signal frequency. If this stage is operating, work back through the r-f stages, as shown at D, C, B, and A, to the antenna terminal.

If any stage fails to pass a signal when using this method, the trouble is localized to that stage, and the individual parts in that stage should be checked for defects.

SIGNAL-TRACING METHOD

A second method of localizing the trouble to a stage is signal tracing. This method is similar to signal substitution, but the procedure starts at the antenna terminal of the receiver, instead of the audio output.

In signal tracing, a signal generator is connected to the antenna terminals of the receiver, and supplies a modulated r-f signal of predetermined amplitude. This signal can then be followed or traced through the various stages of the receiver by connecting an indicating device, described in the following paragraph, first to the input, and then to the output, of each succeeding stage. The point where the signal disappears will indicate the defective stage, and the individual parts within that stage should be checked for defects.

Indicator units used in signal tracing should be of a type suitable for the circuit under test. The audio-amplifier stages require an indicator such as an output meter, speaker, or oscilloscope. Amplifiers operating at radio frequencies require a test instrument that will give an indication at radio frequencies, such as vacuum-tube voltmeters, rf oscilloscopes, detectors with an audio amplifier, or special signal-tracing equipment.

In receivers which operate but do not meet sensitivity specifications, the signal tracing method is used most often to measure the relative gain of the signal through each successive stage of the

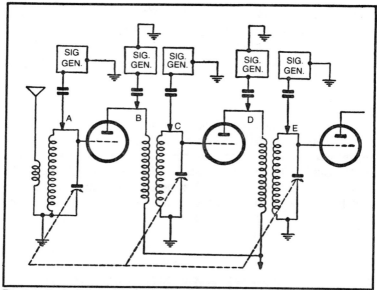

Fig. 3-9. Typical rf amplifier, showing signal-substitution points.

receiver. Included in the service instructions for a receiver there may be a signal tracing chart which contains information on where to apply the input signal, what amplitude the input signal should be, where to connect the indicating device, and what indication should be obtained if the stage is operating properly. With this information, the trouble can be quickly localized to a stage. Then the individual parts within the stage should be checked for defects.

The signal substitution method can also be used to localize trouble in weak receivers if calibrated audio and rf signal generators are used to inject a signal of the frequency and amplitude specified on the signal tracing chart.

CIRCUIT-DISTURBANCE METHOD

Usually, in receivers that are completely inoperative, the trouble can be localized to a stage in the shortest possible time by the signal-substitution method or the circuit-disturbance method.

The circuit-disturbance test is similar to signal substitution. Turn the receiver on and allow sufficient time for the tubes to warm up. Set the volume control for maximum gain and touch the control grid of the output tube with a coin, key, or other metallic object (Fig. 3-10). A click or loud hum should be heard in the headset if the output stage is operating properly. If a click or hum is heard when the output stage is disturbed, follow back through the audio, i-f and rf stages, listening for clicks or hum when the grids are touched. When a point is reached where no clicks are heard, the trouble is between this point and the point at which clicks were last heard, and the individual parts within this section should be checked for defects.

STAGE-MUTING METHOD

Hum, oscillation and noise are common troubles which are sometimes very difficult to locate. The most helpful procedure to follow in trying to determine the cause of one of these troubles is to first localize the trouble to a stage. An efficient and simple method is called stage muting. In using this method, the grid of a stage is effectively shorted to the chassis with a capacitor of approximately $0.25\mu F$. Thus, signals originating further back in the receiver cannot affect or pass this stage. Starting at the output stage, short the grid to the chassis with a capacitor. If the hum or noise continues, the cause must be in the power supply or the output stage. If the hum or noise stops, it is originating at some point preceding this stage. Work back through the set, shorting each grid to chassis in turn, until a grid is reached where the hum or noise does not stop. The point where the hum or noise originates will be between that grid and the preceding grid that was shorted to the chassis.

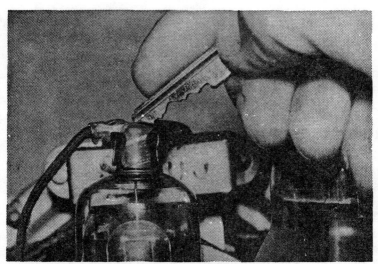

Fig. 3-10. Perform the circuit-disturbance test by touching the control grid of an output tube with a key.

LOCALIZING INTERMITTENT TROUBLES

Conditions of intermittent operation and intermittent noise are probably the most difficult to localize. In many instances it will be necessary to use more than one of the previously discussed methods to localize the trouble to a stage. In some units, intermittent operation or noise occurs only when the unit is cold; in others, only when the unit is hot, or when a signal is applied. Whenever possible, attempt to duplicate the condition under which the trouble is noticeable. Conditions of cold can be duplicated by placing the unit in a refrigerator, or out doors, for a period of time before testing. Conditions of heat can be duplicated by placing the unit in an oven, or by operating the unit for a period of time in a confined area, such as under a cover or in a box. In instances where noise is present only when a signal is applied, tune the signal generator and receiver to the low-frequency end of the band and apply an unmodulated rf signal of sufficient strength to cause the receiver to be microphonic. Then gently tap various components to localize the noise to a stage, section, or part.

Chapter 4
Specific Circuits And Their Problems

The isolation of troubles in individual stages is basically the same regardless of the type of stage in question. Once the defect is known to be in a certain stage, voltage and resistance measurements must be made. The information gathered by making these measurements will, in most cases, pinpoint the trouble to a particular part.

General information on voltage and resistance measurements is given next. In the several paragraphs that follow, those on voltage and resistance measurements are examples of isolating defects in various types of stages used in old-time receivers.

VOLTAGE MEASUREMENTS

The usual procedure is to make the voltage checks first. This will locate the general area of the trouble. When an abnormal voltage condition has been found, the power must be turned off and resistance checks made to determine a short or an open circuit.

In most receivers, voltage measurements are made with the negative lead of the voltmeter connected to chassis ground. The positive terminal is then connected to the points to be measured. In this way, all voltages that are positive with respect to the chassis are measured. If a voltage to be measured is negative with respect to ground, the positive terminal is grounded. If an electronic multimeter is being used, the common terminal is left connected to the chassis and the polarity-reversing switch is set to the positive position for measuring positive voltages or the negative position for measuring negative voltages. The meter range switch must be set to its highest range if the approximate voltage present is not known. This prevents possible damage to the meter. Once an indication is observed on the meter, the range switch should be set to obtain a midscale indication.

Certain voltages are not normally measured with respect to the chassis, and it is important to avoid incorrect readings and possible damage to the meter. For example, the AC power input voltage usually is isolated from the chassis. This is a safety feature that prevents grounding of the power line when power line polarity is not observed, and keeps you from getting a shock when the chassis is touched. This is especially true if the chassis is grounded to the earth. To measure accurately the voltages present, the test leads must be connected directly across the points where the voltage is present. In another example, the filament of a power-supply rectifier tube may be at a high DC voltage with respect to the chassis. If the rectifier filament voltage is measured with respect to ground, the meter may be ruined by the high voltage present. When checking the filament voltage in this case, the meter terminals must be connected to the filament terminals without touching the chassis. One way to prevent meter damage is to remove the rectifier tube, thereby removing any DC voltage present.

If the measured voltage is high or low by more than 20 percent, it is possible that the voltage source is the cause, especially if the equipment is operated from batteries. A voltmeter can be inaccurate also, or it can have a lower sensitivity than the one originally used to make the measurements. This must be taken into consideration when making measurements. For the most accurate results, the voltmeter should have the same sensitivity as the one that was used to make the original measurements.

RESISTANCE MEASUREMENTS

Before making resistance checks, it is very important that the power be turned off and all filter capacitors be discharged. Resistance measurements can be made between certain points and the chassis, or between any two points that are connected by wiring or parts.

ISOLATING TROUBLE IN AUDIO CIRCUITS

The circuit in Fig. 4-1 contains the component parts referred to in this section. Most troubles encountered are due to failure in circuits where DC is present. This means that the trouble can be located by voltage and resistance measurements.

Assume that the stage becomes inoperative. There must be certain DC potentials present for the stage to operate. The first step is to measure the voltage from the plate to ground. The voltmeter range switch must be set to the maximum voltage position because the voltage present is unknown. This precaution is necessary to prevent possible damage to the meter. If there is no voltage present, move the hot voltmeter prod to the point marked B+. If a voltage is indicated, an open circuit exists between that point and the plate of the tube. The screen-grid voltage will be below normal because the drop across screen dropping resistor R3 is greater than the normal drop. Figure 4-1 shows that the plate voltage is applied through resistors R4 and R5. Move the meter hot test prod to the other side of R5. If the reading is zero, R5 is probably open, or C4 is shorted. A resistance check will verify this. If the reading is about normal, move the test prod to the plate again. A voltage reading on one side of R4 and none on the other means that R4 is probably open. A resistance check completes the test. Refer to Chapter 5 for checking resistors.

A shorted C4 could cause the removal of plate voltage from the tube even though the B+ voltage is about normal. The screen-grid voltage also will be affected because it is taken from the same source as the plate voltage. A continuity check of C4 will then show either a dead short or a partial short to ground. In addition, R5 will overheat and many even char and smoke, because if C4 is shorted, R5 will be placed directly across the power supply.

Another cause for complete failure of the stage is the lack of screen-grid voltage when the plate voltage is nearly normal. A shorted screen-grid bypass capacitor C2 will reduce the voltage to zero. This can be checked by measuring the voltage from the screen grid to ground, and double-checked by making a continuity check between the same two points. Refer to Chapter 5 for checking capacitors. If the power is left on for a considerable length of time under these conditions, R3 and R5 will overheat and may even smoke, because they are connected directly across the power supply. This is a definite indication of a short circuit. Because the screen grid has more control on the plate current than the plate has, the plate current will go down; therefore, the plate voltage will be higher than normal.

Another test that can be made is the measurement of the cathode voltage across R2. If the voltage is higher than normal, R2 is probably open. Neither plate nor screen-grid current is flowing; therefore, the plate and screen-grid voltages will be higher than normal. The high-voltage reading is present across R2 because the

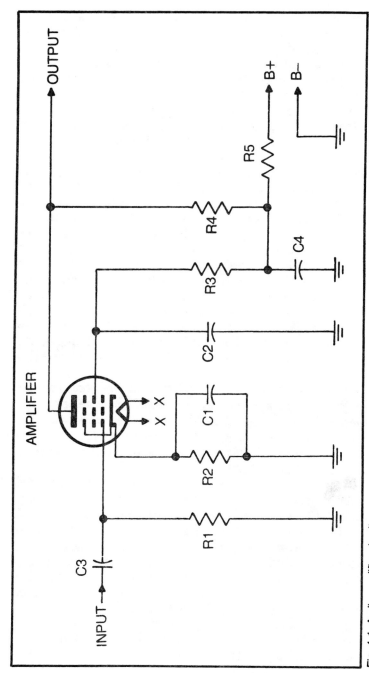

Fig. 4-1. Audio-amplifier circuit.

high resistance of the meter completes the circuit across R2, creating a large voltage drop across the meter. The value of the voltage will depend on the type of voltmeter used. If R2 is shunted by an electrolytic capacitor, the circuit from cathode to ground will be completed by the leakage resistance of the capacitor. The cathode voltage would be only slightly higher than normal, regardless of the type of meter used to measure the voltage.

If the output of the amplifier is distorted, it is probably because the bias has decreased from the normal value. If the plate and screen-grid voltages are found to be lower than normal, bias capacitor C1 is probably shorted. This will produce distortion. Measure the bias between the grid and cathode. The voltmeter must be set to indicate a negative voltage. If C1 is shorted, the voltage will be zero. If the meter needle goes below zero, the grid is positive.

There is only one way the grid can become positive, in addition to gassy tube troubles, and that is for the coupling capacitor to develop a short circuit or leak, allowing the B+ on its other side to leak through to the grid. If C3 is checked with an ohmmeter, it might show an extremely high resistance, which means that it is not leaky. However, when power is applied to the circuit, including the preceding stage, the B+ appears between the ground and the input side of C3. As a rule, any capacitor having equal, or nearly equal, DC voltage from either side to ground should be suspected as being shorted.

If all voltage and resistance measurements are normal but the stage does not operate, coupling capacitor C3 may be open. The simplest, quickest and easiest method to check it is to bridge it with a good capacitor of the same capacitance and voltage rating. If C3 is open, bridging it will produce a signal in the output of the stage if a signal is applied to the input.

If the output is not as great as it should be and the voltage and resistance measurements are normal, it is possible that bypass capacitor C1 is open. If it is open, the decrease in output would be caused by degeneration. Signals that would normally be bypassed around the resistor by a good bypass capacitor will cause a signal voltage drop across the resistor. This voltage drop bucks the applied signal and effectively decreases the amplitude of the signal applied to the stage. As a result, the output also decreases. For example, assume that a 3-volt AC signal is applied between grid and ground. During the positive portion of the AC signal, the grid is 3 volts positive with respect to ground. This causes an increase in plate current through R2, and the developed voltage across it makes the grid negative with respect to ground, say 2 volts. Therefore, the grid is only 1 volt positive with respect to cathode. The 3-volt input signal is seen by the input of the tube as a 1-volt signal.

The most common troubles localized to audio stages are complete inoperation, weakness, hum, motorboating, noise and distortion. The first step in locating the defective part within the stage should be a voltage measurement at each terminal of the tube socket. The manual for a radio set contains a tube-socket layout diagram showing the correct voltages at each tube-socket terminal, and also the resistance of the voltmeter that should be used. Compare the readings obtained from the defective unit with those on the diagram. A slight variation in readings is permissible, but if any great difference is noted, each component part of that circuit must be checked carefully for open or short circuits.

Resistance measurements should follow. To do this quickly, a few moments should be spent examining the circuit diagram to determine the approximate value of the resistance involved. In some circuits that use series and parallel networks, it would be quicker to isolate a portion of the circuit by unsoldering a connection and testing each section separately. Whenever low voltage is read, resistance measurements will determine the faulty component.

Trouble in an audio stage that is weak or completely inoperative can be located quickly by voltage and resistance measurements. This trouble is usually caused by a breakdown or change in the value of a component, and is indicated by incorrect voltage or resistance at one or more points of the circuit. Many times a part will change value only after the unit has been in operation for some time. Defective parts of this type can best be located by taking voltage measurements with a vacuum-tube voltmeter (VTVM). Comparing the readings obtained with those specified in the manual for the radio will then disclose the part across which a higher, or lower, than normal voltage is being developed.

Hum is usually caused by loose shielding or DC circuit wiring accidentally placed close to AC circuits either during repairs or through vibration. A low-frequency hum generally originates from the filament wiring and can be corrected by repositioning grid and plate wires to place them outside the inductive field that exists around wiring in alternating current circuits. All filter capacitors should be carefully checked. An oscilloscope, or vacuum-tube voltmeter with a capacitor in series with one of the test leads, connected between the tube-socket terminals and B— will indicate the presence of hum by a distorted sine-wave pattern, or a reading of the hum voltage.

Motorboating, or low-frequency oscillation, is usually caused by an open grid or cathode circuit. Open capacitors connected between the plate, cathode, or screen grid and ground may also cause motorboating.

When intermittent noise is noticeable in an audio amplifier, it may be attributed to a defective tube, the internal arcing of a component, or loose or high-resistance connections. All tubes, resistors, capacitors and soldered connections should be moved slightly and tapped gently with an insulated prod to locate loose elements in tubes or loose connections at any components.

Audio amplifiers using tubes in parallel or push-pull parallel arrangements usually employ a resistor in series with the plate of each tube to suppress parasitic oscillations. A change in value of this resistor will cause oscillation or distortion. Distortion localized to an audio stage in which the amplification is higher than normal indicates possible failure of components in the inverse-feedback circuit. Reference to the circuit diagram or the manual will show the proper values for components in this circuit, and resistance measurements will indicate the faulty part. In some amplifiers, degeneration is introduced by connecting a small capacitor between the plate of one tube and the grid of the tube in the preceding stage. This is done to reduce distortion originating within the stage at a slight sacrifice in gain.

Distortion in an audio stage is generally caused by improper bias or a defective audio coupling capacitor.

An oscilloscope is useful to determine quickly the sources of hum, noise and distortion in an audio amplifier. To do this, an audio signal generator is connected to the input of the audio amplifier, and the vertical plates of the oscilloscope are connected across the output circuit of the first stage. The audio generator is set at a low frequency, and the sweep-amplifier range control on the oscilloscope is adjusted to produce a stationary pattern on the screen of the cathode-ray tube. Should the pattern appear to be satisfactory, move the vertical-plate connections to the output of the second audio stage, where the sine wave may be observed again. Any distortion in the sine-wave pattern may be credited to the improper functioning of the audio circuits, and should be corrected before proceeding to successive stages.

ISOLATING TROUBLE IN I-F AMPLIFIERS

The method of isolating trouble in an i-f amplifier is similar to that used for an audio amplifier. There will be shorted or open capacitors, open resistors and open inductors: These can be

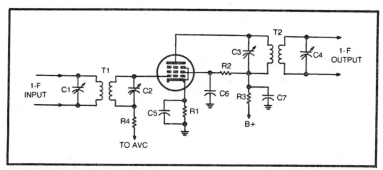

Fig. 4-2. I-f amplifier stage.

detected by making voltage and resistance measurements. An i-f stage is shown in Fig. 4-2.

There is one exception to the above statement, and that is that the i-f stage operates at a fixed higher frequency. The inductors must be turned to the proper frequency. Thus, if trimmers C1, C2, C3 and C4 are not set accurately, the output of the stage will be weak. Some radios have the windings of T1 and T2 tuned by varying the inductance with a powdered-iron slug.

Localizing trouble in an i-f stage requires careful checking of very low resistance values, soldered connections, shielding and circuit components. The resistance of i-f coils is usually very low, and when testing for shorted windings, the ohmmeter should be set on the lowest range and the measurements carefully made. Partially open or shorted coil windings can be quickly checked by aligning the stage and observing the output meter. If it is necessary to turn the trimmer adjustments all the way in or out to reach resonance, the coil is defective. Should the gain of the stage being tested be lower than that of other i-f stages, careful resistance measurements of the windings and trimmer capacitors should be made.

The common troubles in i-f stages are complete inoperation, weakness, oscillation, distortion and intermittent operation.

An inoperative stage is usually due to the absence of voltage at one or more points, or it may result from a shorted or open circuit. The usual voltage and resistance measurements should indicate the defect quickly.

An i-f stage in which the amplication is low is generally caused by improper voltages, partially open or shorted coil windings, or the need for alignment. A stage operating at low gain will give partial voltage and resistance readings, and extreme care should be taken to apply them logically to the apparent trouble.

Oscillation might be caused by loose shielding, a defective tube, or interstage coupling. To check the shielding, place the equipment in operation and move or tap the coil and tube shields by hand. If the frequency of the oscillation changes, the shielding should by cleaned and tightened where it contacts the chassis. All shielded wiring should be examined for cuts, worn spots and poor ground connections. Vacuum tubes can cause oscilliation due to leakage between elements. Tube testers do not always indicate this condition, and the tube should be replaced if no part failure has been found. Interstage coupling may be the cause of oscillation, and it is usually the result of an open rf filter capacitor connected between DC circuits and the chassis. When these capacitors open the circuit, unwanted radio frequencies will be applied to tuned circuits and cause overloading of that circuit.

Distortion is usually caused by improper bias voltage or an open or shorted AVC filter capacitor. Potentials should be measured at the tube socket and followed by resistance measurements, if any differences exist. The grid-load resistor should be measured carefully. Close examination of all soldered connections and mounting hardware is necessary.

Intermittent operation of an i-f stage is often difficult to locate because many components and circuit conditions can cause this trouble. Service and operation reports should be studied. Then the equipment should be placed in operation for a reasonable length of time to allow the trouble to show up without disturbing the circuits. Should the equipment operate correctly during this period, all wiring and components should be moved and tapped gently with an insulated prod. Before the trouble will show up, special operating checks might be necessary, such as placing the chassis in a refrigerator to chill it. If the stage cuts in or out rapidly, it generally indicates a loose connection in the wiring. Should this action be slow, it indicates a dielectric leakage or the opening and closing of a circuit by thermal action. Voltage and resistance measurements made when the receiver is operating correctly will not indicate the trouble. The application of test instruments to an intermittent circuit may create a very small voltage fluctuation that would cause the circuit to resume operation. Therefore, a very careful visual examination of electrical components and soldered and mechanical connections is important.

ISOLATING TROUBLE IN RF AMPLIFIERS

An rf amplifier is similar to an i-f amplifier in practically all respects, except that its tuned circuits can be adjusted to resonate

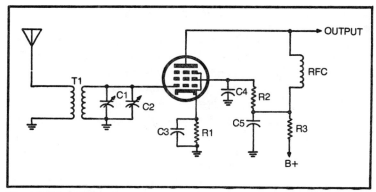

Fig. 4-3. Rf amplifier stage.

over a wide band of frequencies instead of one fixed frequency. Therefore, the troubleshooting method will also be similar.

In the rf amplifier stage (Fig. 4-3) choke RFC is the load. Other circuits may have a transformer winding or a resistor as a load. Regardless of the type of load, defects in them will cause similar symptons.

The combination of the secondary of T1 and C1 and C2 must be tuned accurately to the incoming signal. Capacitor C2 is a trimmer which is set during alignment procedures. If its setting is disturbed, the sensitivity of the stage will be decreased and the signal output will be weak.

ISOLATING TROUBLE IN MIXER STAGES

The mixer combines the incoming signal and the local-oscillator signal to produce the difference frequency.

Troubleshooting a mixer (Fig. 4-4) is similar in most respects to troubleshooting an rf stage. In addition, it is important to check

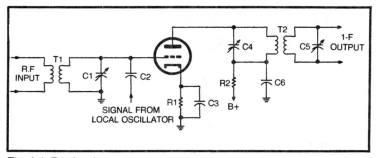

Fig. 4-4. Triode mixer.

coupling capacitor C2. If it should open, there would be no oscillator signal fed to the mixer grid, and the intermediate frequency would not be produced. As in the rf amplifier, it is necessary to keep the adjustments that tune T1 and T2 set to the proper frequencies; otherwise, the output will be weak or not present. Transformer T1 is tuned to the signal frequency, and T2 is tuned to the difference between the incoming signal and the local oscillator frequency. Figure 4-4 shows a triode mixer. A pentode mixer will include a screen grid and suppressor grid; otherwise, the operation will be the same as the triode mixer.

When troubles are localized to a mixer stage, the various frequencies and tube-socket voltages encountered must be considered. The function of a mixer stage is to beat the rf input signal against the signal of the oscillator stage to produce the i-f signal. To obtain this result the tube voltages are critical. Therefore, the first step in localizing trouble within a mixer stage is a comparison of voltage measurements with those specified in charts for the particular radio.

The common troubles in a mixed stage are complete inoperation, weakness, distortion, intermittent operation and noise.

In an inoperative stage, voltage measurements at the tube socket, followed by resistance measurements of the circuits in question, will usually disclose any open or shorted components.

A weak mixer stage will require checks for an inoperative stage plus the examination of wiring for open or grounded circuits. This can be done with an ohmmeter set on the lowest range.

A faulty vacuum tube or improper bias voltages can cause distortion. The tube should be changed if in doubt, regardless of the condition indicated by a tube tester. Defective components in the cathode and control-grid circuits cause improper bias voltage, and each capacitor and resistor should be individually checked to determine its condition. The circuit diagram of the equipment should be closely followed to avoid overlooking a component in the interconnecting grid, cathode and plate circuits.

An intermittent mixer stage should receive the same procedure as outlined for i-f stages. The speed with which an intermittent condition can be corrected depends upon the resourcefulness of the repairman, as no set procedure will correct all intermittent troubles.

Noise that has been localized to a mixer stage might be due to low signal gain in the rf stages. Should a low-gain rf signal be impressed on the mixer stage, the noise frequencies may be amplified more than the signal. This condition should be determined, as it cannot be corrected in the mixer stage.

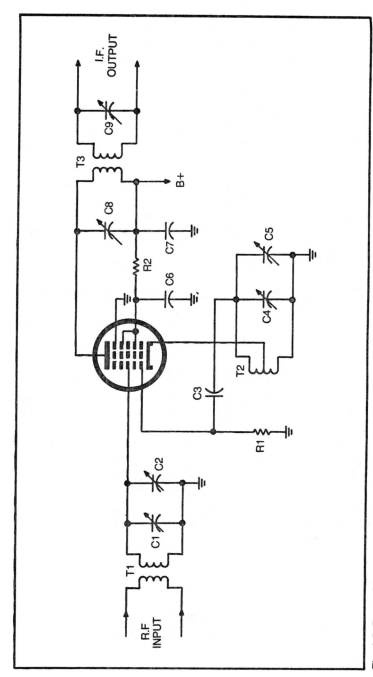

Fig. 4-5. Pentagrid converter circuit.

85

ISOLATING TROUBLE IN CONVERTER STAGES

A converter stage combines the elements of the oscillator and mixer tubes in one envelope. When making voltage and resistance measurements, the socket measurements are made at one socket instead of two.

In a pentagrid converter stage (Fig. 4-5), the oscillator anode is also the mixer screen grid. Therefore, if the screen-grid voltage is absent, there is no voltage at the oscillator anode. The signals are mixed in the electron stream of the tube.

Anything that causes the oscillator to cease operating will prevent the intermediate frequency from being produced and fed to the primary of T3. The first test to make on the oscillator is to measure the bias. The bias must be measured across R1. If you use a voltmeter with less than 20,000 ohms-per-volt sensitivity, the voltmeter could load the circuit to the extent that the oscillator will seem defective when it is operating normally. If there is very little or no bias present, the oscillator is not operating.

If trimmer C5 has been tampered with, the dial calibration on the receiver will be inaccurate and the signal of the wrong frequency will be fed to T3. If trimmer C2 is not set so as to produce maximum output, the output being fed to T3 will be weak.

ISOLATING TROUBLE IN DETECTOR STAGES

The detector demodulates or removes the intelligence from the carrier wave. Thus, when a signal contains voice modulation, the output from the detector will be speech.

Figure 4-6 shows an example of a diode detector. Because there is no high voltage present in this circuit, the chance of component breakdown is not very great. The primary and secondary windings of transformer T must be tuned to the proper frequency to produce maximum output. If R1 or R2 should open, there will be no output. An open circuit in C3 or C5 will reduce the output, but a short circuit in one of them would result in grounding the signal and no output.

The AVC voltage is developed across load resistor R2. If AVC filter resistor R3 opens, there will be no AVC voltage fed to the grids of the controlled stages, and the output will probably increase on strong signals. If AVC filter capacitor C4 short circuits, the AVC voltage will be reduced to zero, and the output may increase, depending on the value of the grid-return resistor in the controlled stages.

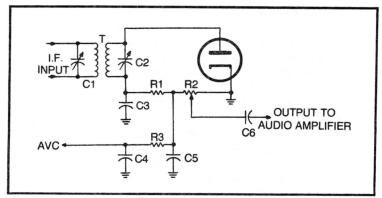

Fig. 4-6. Diode detector.

Old-time radios use different types of detectors, such as plate detectors, grid detectors and diode detectors. In plate detection the rf signal is amplified, then rectified. Grid detection does the reverse: it rectifies the rf input signal and amplifies the audio component. The diode detector offers no amplification of rf or af signals. Many receivers use a twin diode detector to obtain a separate, rectified AVC voltage.

The most common troubles found in detector stages are complete inoperation, weakness, distortion, noise and hum. The first step in determining a faulty component, when trouble has been localized to the detector stage is the comparison of all tube-socket voltages with those shown in the manual for the particular radio. When a defective circuit has been found, resistance measurements of the individual components within that circuit will isolate the defective part.

An operative detector stage is usually caused by an open or short circuit, which can be easily identified by systematic resistance measurements.

A weak detector stage generally indicates that a circuit is partially open or shorted. Each component requires a careful, individual check as the slightest change in value, over the tolerance limits, may reduce the gain of the stage.

Distortion in a detector stage can be caused by improper placement of circuit wiring, high-resistance connections, improper bias voltage and partially open or shorted components. In checking a detector stage for distortion, care should be taken to correct each trouble as it is located, because more than one condition may be the cause of this type of failure.

Noise originating in a detector stage usually indicates dielectric leakage or a loose connection. Ordinary meters will not always indicate trouble of this nature. Therefore, use an oscilloscope or vacuum-tube voltmeter as an indicating device. Connect the indicating device across various component parts of the stage and gently tap or move the parts. An intermittent pattern on the scope screen or fluctuating needle movement indicates the presence of noise in that circuit. If this condition exists when testing across a bypass capacitor, it will indicate it as defective.

Hum is generally caused by radiations from AC wiring, defective grid circuits, loose shielding, or defective filtering. Hum can be isolated to a part of circuit within the stage by using the same procedure as outlined earlier for the noise.

ISOLATING TROUBLE IN POWER SUPPLIES

A power supply delivers operating voltages to the various stages in receivers. The majority of troubles in a power supply occur in the high-voltage rectifier and filter sections.

The most widely used power supply is the full-wave type (Fig. 4-7). The rectifiers are often contained in the envelope of one tube. Troubleshooting is done almost entirely by voltage and resistance measurements.

An open circuit in the primary or secondary winding of transformer T will result in no DC output. Also, if the windings are intact, an open in choke L1 or L2 will open the high-voltage circuit.

If filter capacitor C1 short circuits, the current through tubes V1 and V2 will be very high and will cause the high-voltage winding to smoke, or burn out the tubes. If output capacitor C2 short circuits there will be no DC output, but because of the resistance of the two chokes, the amount of current flowing will be less than if C1 short circuits.

The filter capacitors keep hum out of the operating circuits. Therefore, if either one should open, the output voltage will contain a ripple, and hum will result. There will be a large drop in the output voltage if C1 opens.

Bleeder R discharges the filter capacitors when the power is turned off. This is a safety measure. If the bleeder opens, the DC output point will be dangerous to touch because the capacitors will be fully charged. The bleeder also keeps a load on the output when the regular load is removed.

TROUBLESHOOTING IN POWER SUPPLIES

If the preliminary checks do not locate the trouble, it will be necessary to test the individual components of the unit.

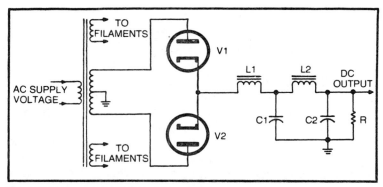

Fig. 4-7. Full-wave-rectifier power supply.

Most troubles in power supplies are caused by a breakdown of parts in the filter circuits. One method of testing filter circuits for defective parts is by checking the resistance of the input and output circuits. By comparing the figures with those specified in the manual, or using a practical application of Ohm's Law for series-parallel circuits, the defective part can be determined. An advantage of this method of testing is that the power supply is inoperative during the test; therefore, no damage can result to any part from excessive current flow should a short circuit exist. Most AC power supplies have small bypass capacitors connected between each side of the input supply line and ground to prevent high-frequency noises from entering the equipment through the power lines. As the DC resistance of the primary winding of the power transformer is comparatively low, the condition of these capacitors cannot be determined by a resistance check across the primary winding. If melted paraffin or compound surrounds the capacitors, they should be removed and checked on a capacitor tester. After checking the power-supply input circuit for continuity and correct resistance, place the ohmmeter test prods across the input to the filter circuit. A reading will be obtained of the equivalent resistance of a complex network, composed of the resistance of the choke, in series with the parallel resistance of the second capacitor leakage and bleeder resistor. As the leakage resistance of normal electrolytic capacitors is relatively high, with respect to that of the bleeder, it will not greatly affect measurements for practical purposes. The ohmmeter will really read the resistance of the filter choke, in series with the resistance of the bleeder resistor.

If the ohmmeter prods are connected across the output terminals of the filter circuit, a reading will be made of the equivalent resistance of the bleeder resistor, shunted by the leakage resistance of the second capacitor, and also shunted by the resistance of the choke, in series with the first capacitor. In this case the ohmmeter will read, for practical purposes, the resistance of the bleeder resistor only. Thus the resistance of the input circuit to the filter is higher than that of the output circuit by the value of the choke.

If the choke was short-circuited, the readings at both input and output would be identical. If the choke was open-circuited, the input readings would be very high (leakage resistance of the first capacitor) and the output reading would remain practically the same. If either capacitor was open-circuited, both readings would remain about the same. If the first capacitor was short-circuited, the input resistance would be low, and the output reading would be the value of the bleeder resistor, in parallel with the choke. If the second capacitor was short-circuited, the input reading would be the value of the choke, and the output resistance would be very low. Likewise, other possible troubles can be found by similar analysis.

Common troubles in filter chokes are open or partially open coils, internal shorts across the terminals of the coils, leaks or partial leaks to the frame of the inductance and shorted turns.

An open choke will cause no voltage output from the power supply, and a partially open choke coil causes low-voltage output. High hum, or ripple, in the output voltage will result if the coil develops a short across its terminals. Sometimes the filter capacitors develop an internal short from one positive lead to the other. This will effectively short out the choke and cause a hum. Capacitors that are used to resonate the choke should also be suspected when this type of trouble is encountered. Some filter circuits use a capacitor across the filter choke to resonate it to the frequency of the hum voltage. Since a parallel-resonant circuit offers very high impedance to its resonant frequency, very little hum voltage will be apparent at the output of the filter. If a large percentage of the coil turns short out, similar trouble may be expected. Leaks or shorts to the choke frame, or iron core, will cause low or no voltage output, and are similar in effect to a shorted or leaky filter capacitor.

If the capacity of the first capacitor is low, the output voltage of the filter will be lower than normal and will have considerable ripple voltage in it. Lack of sufficient capacity in the second filter capacitor will cause the filter circuit to act in a similar manner as to the hum or ripple voltage, but the DC output voltage will be only slightly affected. Sometimes insufficient capacity will cause motorboating, degeneration, or regeneration. If regeneration occurs, the equipment might break into oscillation, whereas degeneration would cause lower amplification. This may cause distortion, if some frequencies are amplified more than others.

Summing up these facts, low amplification, instability and high hum level can be caused by the second filter having insufficient capacity, or having decreased in capacity. These are common troubles when electrolytics dry out or lose electrolyte through evaporation or decomposition, which results in a decrease in capacity and the troubles discussed above. When a capacitor decreases in capacity, it is equivalent to a good capacitor that is partially open-circuited. Shorted filter capacitors are the cause of very low or no voltage output from the filter. Partially shorted filter capacitors cause the voltage to be lower than normal, and the hum level to be high.

CAUTION:
The voltage stored in filter capacitors does not always leak off when the power supply is disconnected from the supply line. To avoid shock, short circuit all capacitors with a low value resistor before handling components of power supply.

ISOLATING TROUBLE IN OSCILLATOR STAGES

The circuit in Fig. 4-8 is that of a widely used oscillator. It is used to assist in troubleshooting oscillators. The parts referred to in the text are marked on the diagram.

In general, the method for troubleshooting an oscillator is the same as that used for an amplifier, because an oscillator is basically an amplifier that has provisions for positive feedback.

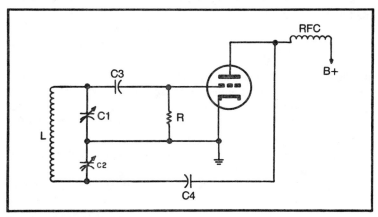

Fig. 4-8. Oscillator circuit.

Connect the test prods of an electronic multimeter across grid-leak resistor R (Fig. 4-8). The grid will be several volts negative with respect to the cathode if the stage is oscillating. If it is not oscillating, there will be little or no voltage present. Do not use a low-resistance meter; the circuit will be loaded down and the stage will cease oscillating if it had been in operating condition.

If the above test shows that the oscillator is not operating, voltage checks must be made. This is a shunt-fed circuit, and nothing is in the B+ line to burn out except the rf choke. If the plate voltage is normal, make resistance checks on the other components.

Capacitor C4 connects the plate of the tube to the lower end of indicator L. If C4 opens, oscillation would probably cease because the feedback circuit will be broken.

Trouble localized to an rf oscillator stage is frequently found to be one of three types: failure to oscillate, weak oscillations, or oscillation at the wrong frequency.

Failure to oscillate results in no output from the receiver or transmitter. The lack of oscillation usually can be traced to an open or shorted coupling between the plate and grid circuit of the tube, an open or shorted grid resistor, an open cathode resistor, a shorted trimmer or tuning capacitor, or a faulty tube. You'll find some tubes that will test satisfactorily on the tube tester, yet when placed in the circuit will fail to oscillate. The first step in isolating trouble in an oscillator stage is to check the socket voltages against the voltage chart for the receiver. Any material deviation from the given standards indicates trouble in that portion of the circuit where incorrect voltage occurs. Localization of the faulty component can be accomplished quickly by continuity and resistance checks fail to disclose any part failures.

Weak oscillation produces a considerable loss of sensitivity in a receiver, with an attendant drop in overall performance. In a transmitter, the output will be extremely low. The fault generally lies in an open or partially shorted coupling between the grid and plate circuits of the tube. Where the coupling is capacitive, a leaky capacitor will decrease the amplitude of oscillation. A partially shorted or open coupling coil will have a similar effect. Check coupling capacitors for leaks, and coils for continuity. Low plate voltage will cause weak oscillation. In converter tubes, low screen voltage or lack of screen voltage produces a like result.

Oscillation at the wrong frequency is characterized by either no response from the receiver or reception of only a portion of the coverage of the receiver at either the lower or upper end of the band, depending upon which side of the fundamental frequency the oscillator is designed to operate. This condition can be caused by a change in the value of components, a partially shorted tank coil or tuning capacitor, an incorrectly aligned oscillator, or a faulty tube, the latter being most evident at the higher frequencies, where a change in the interelectrode capacitance of the tube elements can cause a frequency shift. Check components for value and test for continuity and shorts. A check to determine whether the oscillator is operating correctly can be made by setting the dial of the receiver at a point near the low-frequency end of the dial and feeding a modulated signal of the same frequency from a signal generator into the receiver. Then check the frequency of the oscillator with a frequency meter. The frequency of oscillation should be either the sum or difference of the i-f and rf input signals, depending upon whether the oscillator is designed to operate on the high or low side. In some receivers, the oscillator operates on the high side in the lower bands and on the low side in the higher bands.

LOCALIZING TROUBLE IN AUTOMATIC VOLUME CONTROL CIRCUITS

Many different types of AVC circuits are used in old-time radio sets to vary automatically the grid bias on rf and i-f amplifier tubes, thereby maintaining a constant output signal over a predetermined range of rf input-signal amplitude variation. To correct trouble localized to AVC circuits, first carefully examine the schematic diagram for the particular unit to determine the type of circuit used, and where control voltages can be measured to quickly localize the defective part.

The most common troubles encountered in AVC circuits are complete inoperation and partial operation of the circuit.

Complete inoperation usually has one of two effects on the performance of a receiver, depending upon the nature of the trouble. One condition is extremely high sensitivity and background noise caused by shorted wiring or capacitors. This condition can be quickly located by resistance measurements at various points in the circuit. The other condition is low sensitivity caused by an open resistor or a defective AVC rectifier tube. The first step in localizing trouble of this nature is to determine whether the AVC rectifier tube is functioning. You can do this by measuring the voltage across the AVC load resistor with a vacuum-tube voltmeter. A lack of voltage at this point indicates a defective tube or coupling capacitor. If voltage is present across the AVC load resistor, voltage and resistance measurements made across successive parts of the AVC network will reveal a defective component.

Partial operation of the AVC stage usually results in a distorted output on strong signals and is generally due to a shorted AVC filter capacitor. The defective circuit can be located by connecting a vacuum-tube voltmeter between the control grid of each tube in the AVC network and ground, beginning with the AVC rectifier tube. The absence of voltage on a certain stage indicates an open, shorted, or grounded component, and the careful checking of each part with an ohmmeter will disclose the part failure.

Chapter 5
Testing Tubes and Other Parts

Before you test any tubes or other parts in your antique radio, check the cables (speaker, antenna, etc.) and plugs for good connections and for continuity. Then isolate the trouble to a particular stage or tube as explained in the preceding chapters. If you have done your troubleshooting diligently, you should have a good idea of which tube or other part is at fault, and you shouldn't have to check too many parts before you find the one that needs replacing or repair.

For testing parts, you will need a low-cost general-purpose instrument called the volt-ohm-milliammeter (VOM), or multimeter. Such an instrument is useful for measuring the resistance of parts and checking for short and open circuits. It is also useful for measuring battery voltages, tube DC voltages, and such AC voltages as filament voltages and audio output. The most important specification of a VOM is its sensitivity, measured in ohms per volt. Try to get a meter with an ohms per volt rating of at least 20,000 ohms per volt, such as the Triplett model shown in Fig. 5-1.

Once you have been restoring radios for a while, you may want to acquire additional equipment. Probably the next piece of equipment to buy is an electronic multimeter. This instrument is capable of measuring higher resistances than a VOM—for example, the 0.5 to 5 megohms of the grid-leak resistors found in some sets. Furthermore, an electric voltmeter can measure the voltages in high-resistance circuits more accurately than a VOM (though for low-resistance circuits a VOM is just as good).

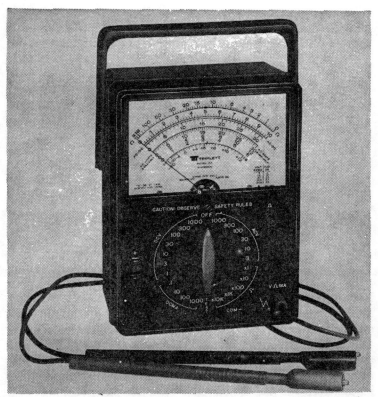

Fig. 5-1. A 20,000-ohms-per-volt multimeter such as this is desirable for testing antique radios (courtesy Triplett Company).

The original type of electronic multimeter was the VTVM. One model VTVM is the Heathkit Model IM-18, shown in Fig. 5-2. Solid-state multimeters are also available. An example is the Heathkit Model IM-5225, shown in Fig. 5-3. These meters are more expensive than vacuum-tube versions, but they are more stable, more reliable and more portable. They feature cordless operation and measure current as well as resistance and voltage.

Before removing any tubes, turn on the power to see whether they warm up properly. If the envelopes are of glass, a visual inspection will shown whether any are burned out. If the tube envelopes are of metal, *turn off the power* before attempting to feel them with your fingers. One-volt or other low-current metal tubes, however, will not generate sufficient heat to do this.

If a tube tester is available, first turn off the power, and then remove and test the tubes *one at a time*. Substitute new tubes only for those that are shown to be definitely defective. If a tube is suspected of being intermittent, it should be tapped gently while being checked, to bring out any defect.

If a tube tester is not available, and modern testers may not test some very old tubes, troubleshoot by the tube substitution method.

TUBE CHECKING BY SUBSTITUTION

Replace the suspected tubes with new tubes one at a time. If the radio begins to operate normally, discard the last tube removed, and return the other original tubes to their sockets. Some circuits, such as some oscillator circuits, may operate with one good tube and not with another. This is because of the difference in the interelectrode capacitance between the tubes, which plays a large part in determining the resonant frequency. Therefore, if a tube does not operate in an oscillator circuit, do not discard it until it is known to be definitely bad.

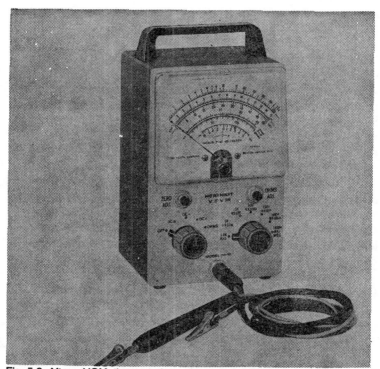

Fig. 5-2. After a VOM, the next piece of test equipment to buy is an electronic voltmeter such as this one. This VTVM from Heath Company is a low-cost electronic multimeter.

In some cases, it is possible to remove a tube from one section
of the equipment without affecting the section being checked. In
such a case, it is possible to troubleshoot the defective section by
using a tube—the same type, of course—from another section as a
substitute, if sufficient spares are not available.

Note that if a replacement for a bad tube becomes defective
immediately, check the component parts in that circuit.

If a component has more than one bad tube at the same time,
substituting tubes one at a time and reinserting the original tube
before substituting for a second tube will not locate the defective
tube. The original tube may have been defective, but it was not
evident because there is another defective tube that is preventing
normal operation. To correct this trouble, install new tubes and keep
putting in new tubes until normal operation is restored. The last tube
replaced is defective and should be discarded. To determine
whether another original tube is bad, return an original tube to its
socket. If there is a noticeable change in operation, discard the last
original tube installed. Another method is to install all new tubes,
then replace them with the original tubes, one at a time. When failure
or change is noticed, discard the last original tube installed. Do not
leave a new tube in a socket if the equipment operates satisfactorily
with the original tube. If not one of the above procedures restores
the receiver to normal operation, further troubleshooting is necessary.

A tube should never be discarded unless a tube tester or other
instrument shows it to be defective, or it can be seen that the tube
has a broken glass envelope, an open filament or a broken base pin.
Do not discard a tube merely because it has been in operation for a
long time. Satisfactory operation *in the equipment* is the final proof of
tube quality.

CHECKING SERIES FILAMENTS

Tube filaments connected in series present a problem. An open
filament in a tube will cause all other filaments in the string to go out.
This makes it difficult to detect a burned-out tube quickly.

One way to test the tubes for open filaments is to remove them
one at a time and check the filaments for continuity with an ohmeter,
but this precedure usually takes too much time. In addition, it can

Fig. 5-3. This FET (field-effect transistor) multimeter is an electronic multimeter from Heath Company. This solid-state meter is more desirable than the vacuum-tube type if you can afford it.

cause burnouts in the 1-volt or other low-current tubes. The ohmmeter stould be set on a scale *other than the lowest*, because the current the ohmmeter can pass through the tubes on its lowest scale is sometimes high enough to burn out the filament.

If the bottoms of the tube sockets are accessible, the tube with the open filament can be found by measuring the voltage across the tube filament terminals with all tubes in their sockets. All good tubes in the string will measure zero voltage across their filaments, but the one that is burned out will have the full voltage that is applied across the string (Fig. 5-4). The open filament will have 6 volts across it. If any one tube in Fig. 5-4 has 1½ volts across it, all filaments are good, because the 6 volts will be divided equally among the four tubes.

Radios using series-parallel filament circuits often have shunting resistors across some tube filaments in the series circuit to maintain the correct value of current flow in each tube. In this type of circuit, the voltage measured across a burned-out filament may be

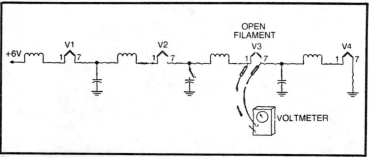

Fig. 5-4. Finding open filament with a voltmeter.

nearly the same as the voltage across a good tube. This is because the shunt resistor may be intact and why measurements should be made carefully and not too rapidly.

TESTING PARTS

When the trouble has been narrowed down to a section and then to a stage by using test equipment or simple short-cut methods, the trouble must be pinpointed to the defective part. This means testing the suspected parts—resistors, capacitors, or inductors. In many cases, the testing can be accomplished with a multimeter. This procedure is useful whether the parts are mounted in a unit or have been removed.

CHECKING RESISTORS

Before checking the suspected resistor with an ohmmeter, the circuit should be examined to determine whether it is necessary to disconnect one lead of the resistor. If it is shunted by another part that can form a DC path, the resistance indicated will be lower than the actual resistance of the resistor, because the total resistance of two or more resistances in parallel is less than the resistance of the lowest value in the branch. When the resistor is disconnected, it can be checked for continuity and resistance. It is advisable to use the ohmmeter range that will give a midscale reading to insure accuracy.

In Fig. 5-5, resistor R4 is shunted across the grid winding of transformer T1. If a continuity measurement is made across R4, the low-resistance path through T1 in parallel with R4 will be indicated on the ohmmeter and an erroneous reading will result. It is therefore necessary to disconnect R4 at one end before checking it. Plate load resistor R5 has no parts in parallel with it and can be checked while it is in the circuit. The resistance from the screen grid to ground is

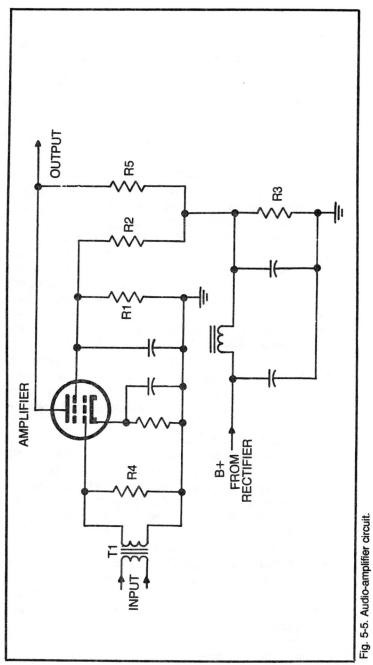

Fig. 5-5. Audio-amplifier circuit.

101

Table 5-1. Power-transformer resistance chart.

Test points	normal indication (ohms)	Test For Short To:
Primary 1-2	5 to 10	Frame (ground) Terminals 3,4, 5, 6, 7, 8, 9
5-volt filament 3-4	less than one	Frame Terminals 5, 6, 7, 8, 9
High-voltage 5-6	50 to 100	Frame Terminals 8. 9
High-voltage 6-7	50 to 100	Frame Terminals 8,9
6.3-volt filament 8-9.	less than one	Frame

measured through R1, which is in parallel with R2 and R3 in series. If the resistance and voltages are different from the specified values, any one of the three resistors could have changed in resistance. To check one of these parts, disconnect one end of it from the circuit.

It is important to use the right scale of the ohmmeter when measuring resistance or continuity. If a high range is used, a low-resistance part or a poor connection will show up as a full-scale or a closed-circuit reading. Use the high range only when checking high-resistance circuits. If a low range is used, a fairly high resistance will give the same reading as an open circuit. The resistance value will be known approximately, either by its markings or circuit information; therefore, you should use the range that will give approximate half-scale indications. Another precaution is to be sure that the fingers do not touch the ends of the test prods, because the resistance of the body will cause an inaccurate indication on the ohmmeter.

Sometimes a resistor will have normal resistance when it is cold, but will change value as its temperature rises. Measure the voltage across it as soon as the power is turned on, and also after it warms up. If the voltage changes considerably over a short time period, the resistor is changing in value and should be replaced.

If voltage or resistance tests indicate that a variable or adjustable resistor may be defective, a final test will have to be made, and for this purpose two of the three leads will have to be disconnected, thus effectively isolating the suspected resistor from the rest of the set. To check the resistor then, measure the resistance from one end to the other and from the top to each of the two ends separately. To test for breaks that show up only as the resistance is varied, slide the moveable member back and forth while testing it.

A resistor measured with an ohmmeter will usually measure a small amount higher or lower than the marking or color code specifies. This is because of the tolerance of the resistor. For example, a 1-megohm unit with a 20-percent tolerance will measure anywhere from 800,000 ohms to 1,200,000 ohms. In addition, the ohmmeter will not be 100-percent accurate, and its deviation from accuracy can cause a further error in measurement. A resistor having a tolerance of 5 percent is marked with a gold band and one with a tolerance of 10 percent is marked with a silver band. Resistors of greater tolerance are not marked.

TESTING COILS AND TRANSFORMERS

Coils and transformers include rf and audio chokes, power transformers, relay coils, audio transformers, i-f tranformers and coils and any component that is wound with wire, except wire-wound resistors. These items should be checked for resistance values and the readings compared with the normal values. If necessary, one lead should be disconnected to prevent errors in readings. If the readings look suspicious, you should check each winding for shorts or leaks to ground, or a leak to another winding within the same component.

Refer to Fig. 5-6 for an example of a power-transformer-winding schematic diagram. Table 5-1 shows the check points, normal readings and the points to check for shorts.

The condition of low-voltage windings is often difficult to determine because usually the resistance is so low that the readings appear as short circuits. However, don't suspect these windings of short circuits unless there is a blown fuse or severe overheating of

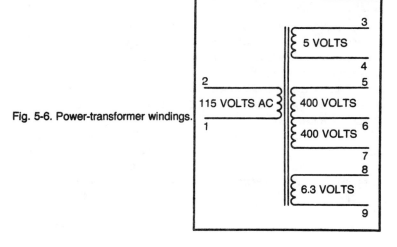

Fig. 5-6. Power-transformer windings.

the transformer. These windings rarely open because the wire is so heavy that a fuse will blow before the winding opens. One method of testing a power transformer for shorts is to connect a 115-volt lamp of 50 to 100 watts in series with the *primary* winding. If the line voltage is 220 volts, a 220-volt lamp must be used. Remove all tubes to take the load off the secondaries.

Turn on the power. If the lamp lights brightly, the high-voltage *secondary* winding is probably shorted. If the condition existed only after the power had been turned on for some time, the test will not show the trouble immediately. It will then be necessary to run this test for several minutes to an hour. If the short circuit takes time to develop, the lamp will glow when the defect appears. This test does not apply to a defective primary. If the primary were shorted, the line fuse would have blown. The troubles that will cause the lamp to glow will therefore be in the secondary windings. If the lamp lights only when the tubes are in their sockets, the transformer is not at fault.

The windings used in rf and i-f amplifier stages are subject to some of the defects found in power transformers. The windings can be tested for open circuits with an ohmmeter. They rarely develop short circuits, but if they are suspected, resistance checks can be used to detect them. When a coil has a very low normal resistance, the available ohmmeter may not be able to indicate accurately the difference between a normal and shorted coil. The only way to be sure is to install a new part. This information applies also to rf choke coils.

CHECKING CAPACITORS

A capacitor can fail in several ways. It may become shorted, develop a leak or an open circuit, or change its capacitance. A multimeter or VTVM can check most leaks or shorts. However, you must use a capacitor checker or AC meter to detect a change in capacitance. If you believe the capacitor open, a good method of double checking it, while it is in the circuit, is to bridge it with a capacitor known to be good.

To determine whether a capacitor is leaky or shorted, disconnect it from the circuit and test is with an ohmmeter. There are occasions when a leak will not show up unless the capacitor is subjected to the voltage appearing in the set; therefore, the ohmmeter test will not indicate a defect. Disconnect doupling capacitor C1 in Fig. 5-7 at the low-voltage side. Connect the voltmeter between the free end of the capacitor, ground the set and turn it on. If there is a

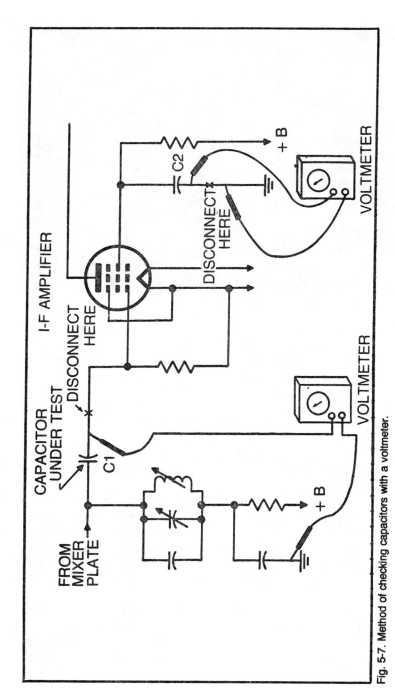

Fig. 5-7. Method of checking capacitors with a voltmeter.

Fig. 5-8. Checking for an open capacitor.

short or leak in C1, part of the DC voltage applied to the other side of C1 will be indicated on the voltmeter.

A suspected bypass or filter capacitor (C2 in Fig. 5-7) should be disconnected at the ground side. Connect the voltmeter between the low side of C2 and ground (Fig. 5-8). With the set turned on, part or all of the screen-grid voltage will be indicated on the meter if C2 is leaky or shorted. Use an ohmmeter to test the capacitor, but turn the power off first.

Whenever a capacitor, such as C1 or C2 in Fig. 5-7, is suspected of being open, the quickest way to check it is to shunt a good capacitor across it (Fig. 5-9).

Capacitors of comparatively large values, such as electrolytics, can be tested for open circuits with an ohmmeter. Be sure to connect the positive lead of the meter to the positive lead of the capacitor. Connect the ohmmeter terminals across the capacitor terminals and watch the meter needle. If the capacitor is good, the needle will rise rapidly as the capacitor is charging, and will fall slowly as the capacitor becomes charged.

Another test is to connect the capacitor across a source of DC power where the voltage is equal to, or less than, the DC voltage rating of the capacitor. If the capacitor is polarized, be sure to connect the plus side to the plus side of the power source. After a few seconds of contact, remove the capacitor and bring its terminals close together. If a spark results, the capacitor is not completely open.

Capacitors may change in value, thereby producing abnormal results. To check the capacitor accurately, it is necessary to disconnect one end or remove it entirely and check it with a capacitor checker. Electrolytic capacitors lose capacitance with age because the electrolyte dries out.

A variable tuning capacitor or air trimmer can become shorted or leaky. To test for either condition, one end of the capacitor must

Fig. 5-9. Shunting a good capacitor across a questionable one.

Fig. 5-10. Checking for a shorted tuning capacitor.

be disconnected from the circuit to prevent a DC path through a coil or other part. The operation is the same as for other capacitors; that is, the ohmmeter test leads must be connected from one set of plates to the other. Any accidental bent plates must be straightened and foreign matter removed from between them. While observing the meter needle, move the rotor plates through their complete range (Fig. 5-10). When the abnormal condition has been remedied, the ohmmeter will read infinity.

Chapter 6
A Handy Guide to Common Problems

The troubleshooting process can be speeded up greatly if you know what parts and what defects in them are likely to cause certain operational problems. For example, if the sound from a radio set is distorted, only a few defects can cause this. If you know what they are, then you'll know where to begin looking for the trouble and what measurements to make. This chapter provides a handy guide to the problems of weak reception, distorted sound, intermittent operation, hum, and noise. The information in this chapter should help you get your collectible radios operating shipshape in record time.

The best way to begin troubleshooting is to inspect the receiver thoroughly. See that the power plug is in place, examine the fuses and turn on the receiver. Look and smell for evidence of burning. See that all tubes are in the right sockets. Note whether the set has been burning or smoking. Burning can be the result of arcing from the chassis through the wire insulation, an overloaded resistor, or a shorted transformer winding. When a resistor becomes greatly overloaded and smokes it is usually because of a shorted filter or bypass capacitor, but the smoking can also be caused by a winding shorting to the chassis or to another winding.

TROUBLESHOOTING A WEAK RECEIVER

The procedure for troubleshooting a weak receiver is basically the same as that used for a dead receiver; that is, it is a matter of localizing the trouble by stages. But note this difference: When troubleshooting a dead set, you are not too concerned about the amount of output that results from a particular test, so long as there is an output; when troubleshooting a weak set, you may find it important to know the precise amount of output produced when a signal is injected into the stage. It is assumed that the tubes in the suspected stages have been tested before stage gain tests are made.

Before troubleshooting procedures are begun, some preliminary steps should be taken to insure that the defect is not an operating fault. Listed below are some checks that you can make before you begin troubleshooting.

— See that the receiver is tuned properly.
— Be sure that all switches are properly set.
— Check the line voltage to see that it has not dropped.
— Determine whether signals are weak on only one or more stations.
— Check the antenna to see that it is still connected.

Troubleshooting Without Stage Gain Data

It is usually possible to locate the trouble in a weak receiver without stage gain information. In such cases, a signal is injected into the various stages, the point being noted at which the signal input must be *increased* instead of decreased to produce the same output. For example, an audio signal from an af signal generator applied to the plate of an audio amplifier produces a certain output from the receiver. When the same signal is applied to the input of the same stage, it should produce a stronger output than before—the signal generator output must be reduced to keep the output at the same level. If the generator output must be increased to produce the same output, the trouble is between the input and output of this stage.

Troubleshooting by Using Stage Gain Data

Sometimes it is almost impossible to determine whether a stage has the proper gain, either because it is normally low, or because the slight difference from normal output cannot be noticed. Then you must take detailed stage-gain measurements to determine which part of the receiver is not amplifying properly. To do this, the technical data for a receiver must specify the minimum and maximum signals required at certain points to produce a given output. It is important to set all controls and switches as the receiver manual recommends.

As the tests progress toward the antenna section, there is less signal input required to produce the same output. This is because the signal is being amplified by passing through more stages. The output of the signal generator should be compared with the information in the radio manual. Readings that are out of limits by a small amount do not necessarily indicate that the receiver is not operating properly.

The gain of the individual stages of a receiver over a period of time will vary. If the difference is great and the receiver's overall output is weak, the stage probably is at fault. When a stage lacks gain by a considerable amount, voltage and resistance checks might be necessary to locate the faults.

In the case of a weak receiver, the tubes should be checked before any other action is taken. Voltage and resistance measurements will show such faults as leaky bypass capacitors and resistors that have changed in value. These conditions can reduce the plate and screen-grid voltages to the extent that the output will decrease and cause the signals to become weak.

In Fig. 6-1, capacitor C603A can cause the above troubles in the plate circuit of first af amplifier V601A and af cathode follower V601B.

An open bypass capacitor is hard to locate, because there is no telltale indication of its condition in the DC voltage and resistance readings. But there are other symptoms that can be detected.

- Capacitor C609 is the cathode bypass in V601A, the first i-f amplifier. If C609 should open, there would be a signal voltage drop across cathode-biasing resistor R604, the voltage drop will cause degeneration and this in turn will reduce the output noticeably.
- If the cathode bypass in the first i-f amplifier should open, the signal would be considerably weaker than it would have been in the case of C609. This is because any signal present in the i-f section of a normally operating set is considerably weaker than it is in the af section, and any loss occurring in the i-f section is therefore the more noticeable.

An open coupling capacitor between stages usually will cause the output to drop to zero, but in the case of a very strong signal, the signal may get by the open capacitor and produce a weak output. However, signals other than the very strong ones will not get through with very much strength. Then you can consider the set weak.

111

TROUBLESHOOTING A DISTORTED RECEIVER

Only a few defects can cause distortion, and they can usually be identified by the sound of the receiver output. Distortion is present when the output signal is muffled or raspy, or does not sound as it should. The experienced troubleshooter can often tell from the sound just what type of distortion is present and what causes it. In most cases the distortion will be in the audio section. Distortion is usually caused by an upset in bias, or by overloading of a stage.

Types of Distortion

Frequency distortion occurs when all frequencies are not amplified to the same extent. For example, if the high and low audio frequencies originally were of the same strength, but in the output of the receiver the low frequency notes are reproduced louder than those of the high frequencies, frequency distortion is present.

Amplitude distortion is present when there is a change in the harmonic content of the signal after it passes through one or more stages. This type of distortion is the more bothersome because the signal sounds unpleasant, whereas frequency distortion is only a matter of some frequencies being stronger or weaker than others.

Common Causes of Distortion

- **Leaky Coupling Capacitor.** One of the most common causes of distortion is a leaky audio coupling capacitor such as C605 (Fig. 6-1), which couples the signal from the af amplifier V602A to the af output amplifier V603. If C605 becomes leaky, it will act as a resistor in series with grid resistor R613 and plate load R611. This series circuit is connected across the B+ line, making the grid end of R613 less negative than it was, or even positive. The tube now operates on the upper portion of the response curve, producing distortion.
- **Gassy Tube.** If the output tube V603 or any other tube becomes gassy, amplitude distortion will result. The bias will be reduced, and the grid might draw current and produce distortion.
- **Other Causes.** Other causes of distortion are misalignment, poor power supply filtering, warped speaker diaphragms, oscillation, excessive strength or input signals and interference from crosstalk.

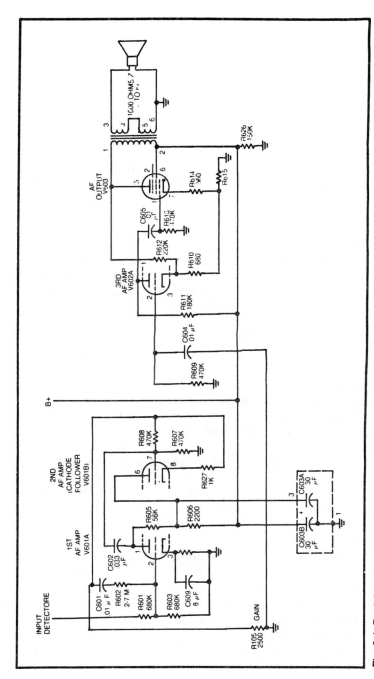

Fig. 6-1. Partial receiver circuit, illustrating procedures described in text.

113

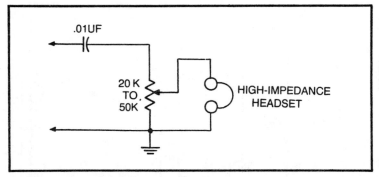

Fig. 6-2. Audio signal tracer.

Localizing Distortion

Localizing distortion is more difficult than troubleshooting a dead or weak receiver. Signal substitution can be used, but it is more convenient to use a form of signal tracing. Connect an antenna to the receiver input and connect a home-constructed audio signal tracer (Fig. 6-2) to various points to determine where the trouble lies.

Assume that the output at the speaker terminals is distorted and the trouble is in the audio channel, which includes V602A and V603, and gain control R105. Connect the prods of the signal tracer to pin 5 of V603 and ground. If the signal is present at the output, the secondary of the output transformer is probably in good condition. Move the hot prod from pin 5 to pin 1 of V603.

If the output is not clear, the plate circuit of V602A is not operating properly, and the trouble could be in the input circuit of V602A.

A more positive method of detecting distortion is by using an oscilloscope and an audio signal generator. The equipment setup is shown in Fig. 6-3. Connect the signal generator to the vertical amplifier terminals of the oscilloscope by setting S1 to position 1. This switch is set to position 2 to connect the oscilloscope across the plate load resistor of the stage being checked.

First, adjust the signal generator to 400 Hz. Set S1 to position 1 and adjust the oscilloscope frequency controls to produce on the screen two sine waves that look like those at A in Fig. 6-4. Adjust the oscilloscope controls to show clean sine waves. We are assuming at this point that trouble is not present. Compare the results with the patterns shown in Figure 6-4.

Assume that the trouble has been isolated to the audio channel. Connect the output of the signal generator to V602 (first af input) and

114

set S1 to position 2. Connect the test probe to the plate (pin 5) of V603 and observe the waveform. If, for example, the waveform is unlike pattern A when the probe is connected to pin 5 of V603 and is like pattern A when the probe is connected to pin 2 of V602A, the distortion is between those two points. The patterns in B, C and D show the waveforms that will appear on the oscilloscope screen when there is distortion; they also indicate some of the causes of distortion.

Diagram D in Figure 6-4 shows a distorted sine wave as it appears on an oscilloscope. When such a condition arises, the trouble may be in the AGC system (if present) because the AGC normally prevents overloading by keeping the output from all signals at a constant level.

TROUBLESHOOTING AN INTERMITTENT RECEIVER

A receiver is operating intermittently if from time to time it operates normally, but between times goes dead or develops any other type of trouble. Intermittent troubles include all types to which a receiver is subject, but they appear and disappear at irregular, or even regular, intervals. Such troubles are hard to trace, because

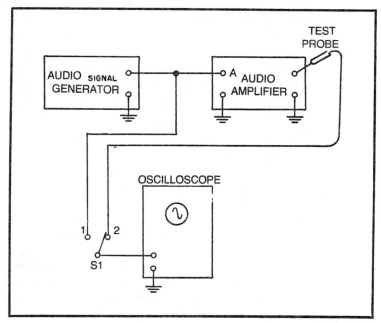

Fig. 6-3. Setup for checking distortion.

they do not exist when the set is operating normally, and because the set may resume normal operation before you can finish testing it.

Causes of Intermittent Operation

- **Capacitors.** A frequent cause of intermittent operation is the haphazard opening and closing of a connection within a fixed capacitor. For example, the circuit would open if a pig-tailed lead pulled loose from the foil, and then a slight jarring of the set might cause the contact to be made again. That same effect might be caused by a sudden switching off and on of the voltage. If capacitor C604 in Fig. 6-1, which couples the audio from gain control R105 to the grid of af amplifier V602A, should become intermittent, the signal level would vary up and down. If the opening and closing condition is at a rapid rate, the effect may appear as noise. If the screen-grid bypass in the i-f amplifier should open and close at slow intervals, oscillations will occur. If it opens and closes in rapid succession, noise will be produced. Variable tuning capacitors can short intermittently because of dust, dirt, or other foreign particles becoming lodged in between the plates. The plating on the plates sometimes peels off in slivers which are often long enough to cause intermittent short circuits. The rotor wiping contacts may have improper spring tension or corrosion that could cause intermittent high-resistance contact to the capacitor frame. In very small variable capacitors, the plates have extremely close spacing; these plates can become bent and may short if the frame should warp because of heat or twisting of a subchassis. Small air capacitors, used as trimmers, and compression-type trimmers also collect dirt. The troubles will be the same as those in turning capacitors.
- **Loose Connections.** A loose connection in any portion of the set can cause intermittent operation.
- **Resistors.** Wire-wound resistors sometimes develop intermittent open circuits at the junction of the resistance wire and the terminals. Carbon resistors may develop opens, but they usually occur after the resistor becomes hot during a long period of operation. Some carbon resistors are insulated and have the resistance element in the form of a carbon rod in the center. The carbon rod can crack and cause intermittent operation.

- **Tubes.** Normally, in troubleshooting, the tubes are suspected first. If a tube is intermittent it may be normal when tested, and the test will be of no value. An intermittent tube can sometimes be found by tapping the suspected one.

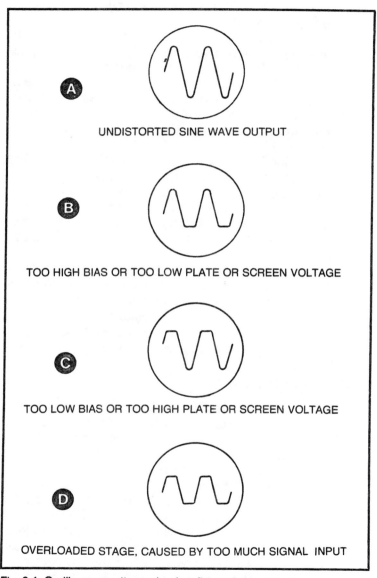

Fig. 6-4. Oscilloscope patterns showing distorted sine waves.

Elements in a tube may expand because of heat, and short to other electrodes momentarily. The filament may expand and break. Then as it cools, the ends may come together again and current flows, producing normal results. Depending on conditions, this may occur several times per minute for a particular tube.

- **Inductors.** Rf and AC coils that carry DC are especially susceptible to intermittent opens. The form on which the coil is wound may expand from the heat and snap the winding. Moisture on the surface of the wire produces a chemical action which causes corrosion that will eat away the conductor. An arc may form and close the circuit momentarily; when the carbonized area breaks down, the circuit opens again.

- **Potentiometers.** Carbon volume or gain controls often have resistance strips that may become pitted because of wear. Only a small portion of the moving arm may be in contact with the strip, and a slight jarring of the set may break the contact momentarily. This condition will be present especially in controls where DC current flows and arcing could occur.

- **Solder Joints.** Original solder joints often appear good to the eye, but under the surface there may be a looseness which could eventually cause intermittent operation. Technicians often introduce intermittents by poor soldering. Therefore, carefully examine all solder joints, particularly those that have been made during repairs.

Isolating Intermittent Troubles

- **Audio Signal Substitution.** Connect an electronic multimeter to the output circuit of the last i-f amplifier. If during intermittent operation, the meter needle remains steady, the trouble is between the last i-f amplifier and the audio output. An arcing in the power supply would have an effect on the output. If the trouble is traced to the audio section, the signal tracer that was used to trace distortion can be used by following the instructions given in *Localizing Distortion*. Rather than use the incoming signal from a transmitter in this procedure, however, it is better to apply an audio signal from a signal generator between the detector output and ground. This is because the signal from the generator will normally be at fixed amplitude, while the incoming signal may vary over a wide range. If the meter needle varies in step with the output signal, the intermittent condition is somewhere between the last i-f amplifier and the antenna.

- **RF Signal Substitution.** The same procedure is used as in troubleshooting a dead set. A signal of the proper frequency is fed into the antenna jack with the antenna disconnected. A modulated or unmodulated signal can be used. If it is modulated, the signal can be heard in the speaker. If the signal is unmodulated, a VTVM connected across the detector load will indicate an output. When the set is intermittent, the trouble will show up as variations on the meter. Move the signal generator lead to the rf amplifier grid. If the meter needle is now steady, the intermittent is between the rf amplifier grid and the antenna jack. If the output is still intermittent, the trouble is between the signal generator and the detector load. Move the signal generator output to the grid or the mixer. If the meter needle does not fluctuate in step with the intermittent signals, the trouble is between this point and the rf amplifier grid. If the meter needle follows the variations, the trouble is between the mixer grid and the dector load. This procedure is used to localize the defective stage, working toward the meter connection.
- **Forcing Troubles to Reappear.** There are times when the intermittent condition does not reappear for hours or even days. Often it can be made to reappear by placing a cardboard box over the receiver to concentrate the heat. This trick works best when the condition is caused by shorts or opens resulting from heat under the chassis. If the receiver is sensitive to jarring, rap the chassis at several points to make the intermittent reappear.

If one end of the chassis seems more sensitive to rapping, the trouble is probably, though not necessarily, at that end. Moving resistors and capacitors around with an insulated prod will often reveal poor contact in the components. If there is a sharp disappearance of the signal or a sudden change in noise, move the wiring around with the prod. Do not move the wires too far out of place, as this may cause other troubles. You can often find poor solder connections by wiggling the wiring at the sockets and other terminals.

The chassis may seem to be equally sensitive to jarring at all points. It is then necessary to keep prodding around, stage by stage, until the bad point is found.

Certain components will open intermittently during line voltage surges and will later be restored to normal. Remove and replace tubes one at a time. If the receiver becomes insensitive to tapping when a particular tube is removed, the trouble is in that stage or a stage closer to the antenna.

TROUBLESHOOTING A RECEIVER FOR HUM

Before the receiver can be freed of hum, it is first necessary to know what hum is and how to recognize it. The experienced radio repairer recognizes it as a steady low-pitched sound. Hum is produced by power line AC variations and is usually 60 to 120 hertz. It is a tone that has a constant amplitude and is of one frequency. This distinguishes it from noise, which consists of an unpleasing sound of many random frequencies and is constantly changing in amplitude. Hum can also be regarded as a low-frequency audio voltage. In this receiver, as in most other AC receivers, the hum will have a frequency of 60 to 123 hertz.

Hum may develop directly in the audio frequency section of a receiver because of

— Inadequate filtering in the power supply.
— Stray coupling from the AC power leads.
— Short circuit between the heater and cathode of a vacuum tube.
— The signal present in the rf and i-f circuits being modulated by the hum.

Causes of Hum

- **Filter Capacitors.** The most likely cause of hum in any AC receiver is an open filter capacitor. The capacitors are in the filter circuit for removing the hum from the output of the rectifiers. Capacitors C1 and C2 (Fig. 6-5) are examples of filter capacitors. If either capacitor should open, the hum level would rise considerably. The schematic diagram shows that C1 and C2 are mounted in the same can. If leakage should develop *between* the two capacitors, the result would be similar to connecting a resistor across choke L2. This would reduce the effectiveness of the choke and cause a ripple in the output of the filter, producing hum. Excessive DC can be forced through choke L1 if filter capacitor C1 becomes leaky. The excessive DC through the choke causes core saturation, which lowers the inductance,

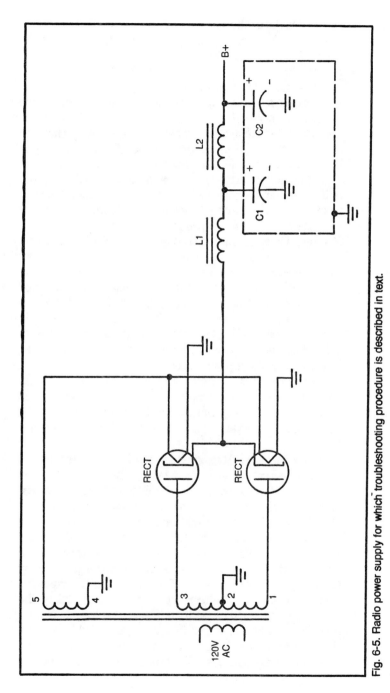

Fig. 6-5. Radio power supply for which troubleshooting procedure is described in text.

121

and makes the choke less effective as a filter. These last two examples show that the hum is apparently caused by the choke, but the actual trouble is a leaky capacitor.

- **Filter Chokes.** If any one of the filter chokes becomes shorted internally, the receiver will hum. Internal shorting seldom occurs; tests required to determine whether the coil is defective should be carried out only after other components have been checked. Iron-core chokes usually have an air gap in the core to prevent core saturation. The gap is kept open by a wedge of nonmagnetic material such as paper, copper or brass. If the gap material should drop out or if it were not there in the first place, the gap could close up from vibration of the core laminations. This would allow core saturation, which would produce hum.

- **Power Transformer High-Voltage Winding.** This power supply uses a full-wave rectifier, which means that the frequency of the rectifier output—the input of the filter—will be 120 hertz if the power line frequency is 60 hertz. If the winding numbered 1, 2, 3 should open between points 1 and 2 or between 2 and 3, an abnormal hum would result. Testing and replacing all chokes and filter capacitors will not correct the trouble, because the opening of one leg of the high-voltage winding changes the circuit to that of a half-wave rectifier. The output frequency is now 60 hertz, and the chokes and capacitors are not large enough to filter such a low-frequency hum. This condition could also be caused by a cathode-to-plate short in a full-wave rectifier tube.

- **Tube Cathode-to-Heater Leakage.** A 60-hertz hum can be caused by cathode-to-heater leakage in a tube, especially in the audio stages, which can readily pass low frequencies. As an example, the first audio frequency amplifier V601A in Fig. 6-1 would produce a 60-hertz hum if the cathode were to short to the heater. This tube is shown in Fig. 6-6. If the cathode and heater should touch, the heater and the cathode-bias resistor R604 would be in parallel as shown by the connection in the figure. This would put 6.3 volts AC across R604. The 60-hertz voltage would modulate the electron stream and cause hum. This could happen in an rf tube also, in which case the 60-hertz signal would modulate the rf when a signal is tuned in, and be demodulated by the detector. If a stage has no cathode-bias resistor and the

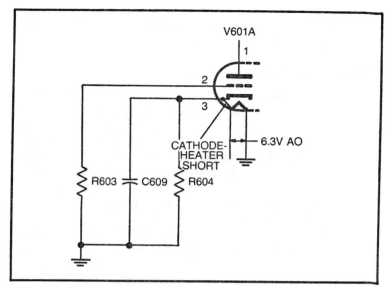

Fig. 6-6. Heater-to-cathode short.

cathode is grounded, the same defect would not be noticed because there is no place across which the 60-hertz voltage can develop.

Determining Frequency of Hum

When a hum is heard in the output of a receiver, the first step is to determine its frequency. In a set using a half-wave rectifier, there can be only one hum frequency: the line voltage. In this receiver in which the rectifier is a full-wave type, the rectifier output is 120 hertz when the input voltage frequency is 60 hertz.

If you do not have sufficient experience to be able to recognize the frequency, you can use the audio signal tracer shown in Fig. 6-2. Connect the tracer across a 6.3-volt AC source. One lead can be connected to the chassis and the other one to the ungrounded filament terminal of a 6.3-volt tube. A loud 60-hertz hum will be heard in the headset. If the hum in question sounds like the hum just heard, it is of the same frequency; if the frequency is higher, it is a 120-cycle hum.

If a 120-hertz hum is present, it means that the defect is probably in the power supply filter and that the filtering is inadequate. If a 60-hertz hum is present, the defect is not in the power supply; it is probably a cathode-to-heater short in a tube, or stray AC pickup by a tube grid. The one exception to this rule is covered in *Power Transformer High-Voltage Winding*.

Tracing Power Supply Hum or Audio Hum

- **Sectionalization.** Turn the gain control, such as R105 in Fig. 6-1, all the way counterclockwise. If the hum is still heard, it is coming from the power supply or the audio channel. If the hum is present in the audio channel and it is a 120-hertz hum, it is due to inadequate filtering in the power supply. If the hum is present with both gain controls turned on, and it is a 60-hertz hum, it *could* be from a cathode-to-heater short in a tube, or stray coupling to a grid, but it is more probably in the audio section.

- **Isolation.** If the hum has been traced to the audio section and is a 60-hertz hum, it will be necessary to find the stage where it originates. A quick and easy method of hum isolation is one that uses an audio signal tracer such as the one shown in Fig. 6-2. Connect one probe of the tracer to a convenient point on the chassis. Touch the other probe to pin 1 of af output tube V603. If the hum is not heard, it is originating between this point and the detector. Touch the probe to pin 2 of V602A. If the hum is not heard, it is coming from somewhere between this point and the detector. Touch the probe to pin 2 of V602A. If the hum is not heard, the hum is originating between this point and the previous test point. If the hum is heard, it is originating somewhere between this point and the detector. Move the probe successively to the input of the remaining stages toward the detector until the hum is not heard. This system eliminates the stages between the test point and the speaker whenever the hum is heard.

Tracing Modulation Hum

Modulation hum modulates, or varies, the rf carrier at the hum frequency. Because the carrier is rf, it can pass through the rf and i-f sections; the detector will then demodulate the signal and the hum will be heard.

- **Sectionalization.** Turn the audio gain control to the maximum clockwise (on) position. If the hum is present with the control turned on but is not present when the control is off, the hum is originating between the control and the antenna. Pull out the last i-f amplifier tube. This will stop the hum from getting through. Any hum originating in the rf section can get through only by modulating the rf carrier, and will have a frequency of 60 hertz. Therefore, the hum discussed below will have a frequency of 60 hertz.

- **Stray Coupling Hum.** One of the most important causes of hum is induction into the rf or i-f section. Filter circuits or capacitors are usually at the AC power input to prevent this. If a capacitor in this circuit should open, hum would result. The simplest method of determining which of them is at fault is to bridge them, one at a time with a good capacitor.

TROUBLESHOOTING A NOISY RECEIVER

A receiver is noisy when the output, in addition to the desired signals, contains crackling, sputtering or frying sounds. Noises fall into two general categories—external and internal. External noise is from a source outside the receiver. Internal noise is from a source inside the receiver. Noise is made up of many frequencies ranging from audio to rf; therefore, it can pass through any stage even though it does not modulate the carrier.

Causes of External Noise

External noise is divided into two classes—atmospheric and man-made.

Atmospheric noise is caused by lightning and other natural electrical disturbances. Little can be done to reduce noise from atmospheric conditions. Usually it can be avoided by moving the receiver to another location, or by changing the operating frequency to one that is relatively free from interference.

Man-made noise can be produced from many sources, such as loose or arcing power lines, gasoline-engine ignition systems, electric motors and generators, other radio sets, diathermy machines, etc. Frequently, this type of noise is suppressible.

Loose or corroded connections in the antenna and ground systems are a frequent cause of external noise.

Causes of Internal Noise

- **Transformers.** Noise in transformers is frequently caused by corroded breaks in the windings. Primary windings in i-f, rf and radio transformers are the worst offenders. The corrosion causes the winding to open, leaving a small gap across which the current may be conducted by the corrosion itself, or an arc may jump intermittently, producing sharp, rapid changes in current, and therefore noise. Transformer windings can work loose from their terminals, producing noise resulting from intermittent connections.

- **Wire-wound Resistors.** Wire-wound resistors are subject to the same noise troubles that occur in transformers. When a resistor winding works loose from a terminal, the result is a rapid rate of intermittent operation which causes noise.
- **Potentiometers.** Potentiometers are among the main sources of noise. The constant friction between the sliding arm and the resistance element causes wear and noise. As the resistance element becomes badly worn, the contact becomes very poor and, ultimately, intermittent. Noise results even when the control is not being adjusted.
- **Band Switches.** When the contacts on a band switch or a similar switching device become corroded and worn, a noise will be generated when it is set from one position to another. When the switch is dirty, it may be noisy. The contacts may become bent, causing an intermittent condition that produces noise.
- **Tuning Capacitors.** Though it seldom happens, tuning capacitors can become noisy, especially when the rotor plates are turned. Warping of the plates, shifting of the rotor shaft, and particles of metal slivers peeling from the plates are common sources of noise. Dust and dirt often carry fine metal particles, and if they become lodged in between plates, noise results as the rotor is turned.
- **Tubes.** Electron tubes generate noise that has several possible causes.
- **Shot effect** is produced because electron current consists of separated particles that leave the cathode in a random fashion, producing fluctuating currents uniformly distributed over all frequencies.
- **Flicker effect** is a low-frequency noise caused by small emitting areas of the cathode constantly changing their emission characteristics.

In tubes having more than one collector element, such as the screen and plate of a pentode, the random division of current produces uniform noise currents over the whole frequency spectrum of a tube output.

126

- **Microphonics** are low-frequency noises produced by motion of the elements of a tube. These are heard when the tube is subjected to vibration.

    Other sources of noise in tubes are positive-ion-emission currents, positive-ion currents produced as the result of gas ionization and secondary-electron emission.
- **Poorly Soldered Joints.** Poorly soldered joints may be a very serious cause of noise. Such noise results from movements of the joint beneath a soldering job which looks good on the surface but is actually not well done.
- **Mechanically Caused Noises.** Tube shields that are not securely locked in place can move and cause scraping noises when the set is jarred. Loose screws and subchassis cover plates will produce the same scraping noises. The thing to remember is that noise is always caused by the rapid making and breaking of a circuit somewhere. Some common types of noise, and their probable causes, are listed in Table 6-1.

Isolating External Noise

Refer to Fig. 6-1. Turn gain control R105 to a point where the noise is heard. Disconnect the antenna from the antenna terminals. Short out the terminals with a jumper. If the noise stops or is reduced considerably, it is originating outside of the receiver. Remove the jumper and reconnect the antenna. Shake the antenna lead. If the noise gets worse, the transmission lead has a break in it or it is rubbing against a tree, pole, or other object. It is also possible that the antenna is rubbing against something, or a connection between the antenna and the lead-in is loose.

If the preceding tests indicate that the noise source is outside of the receiver, the noise is probably radiated noise picked up by the antenna. The trouble now is in the immediate vicinity and may be coming from a a nearby power line, vehicle ignition system, motor, generator, or hospital equipment. If a portable or mobile receiver is available, take it to various areas that may be radiating noise. When a

Table 6-1. Mechanically caused noises.

Type of Noise	When Noticed	Probable Causes
Scratching	When signal is being tuned in.	Dirty tuning capacitors.
Scratching	When adjusting gain control.	Worn gain control.
Scraping	When changing bands.	Worn wave-band switch.
Intermittent crackling, scraping	When chassis is jarred.	Loose tube elements, screw or shield can.

point is reached where the noise level increases in the test receiver, the noise source is nearby.

Disconnect the ground wire. If the noise *decreases*, the ground connection is probably poor or the ground lead is too close to a noise source. If the noise *increases*, it is probably entering on the power line.

Localizing Internal Noise

Turn gain control R105 to a point where the noise is heard. Disconnect the antenna from the antenna terminals. Short out the terminals with a jumper. If the noise continues, it is originating in the receiver.

Turn gain control R105 to the extreme counterclockwise position. If the noise continues, it is originating between the gain control and the speaker. If the noise does not continue, it is originating between the antenna and the gain control. Use the method described later in *Stage Blocking* for locating this source of noise.

Isolating Noise

- **Signal Tracing.** In the audio stages, the audio signal tracer shown in Fig. 6-2 can be used to localize noise by the same method used to localize distortion and hum. Connect the ground terminal of the signal tracer to a convenient point on the chassis. Remove the af output tube. Insert the signal tracer probe in pin 5 or 6 of the socket. If noise is heard, the power supply may be at fault. Check the power-supply tubes by substitution, and inspect all connections, particularly the connecting plugs and jacks. If noise is not heard, replace the af output tube. Touch the signal tracer probe to pin 5 of af output tube V603. If the noise is not heard in the headset, the noise originates in the secondary of T601 or the speaker circuit. If the noise is heard, it originates in the primary of T601 or between pin 5 and the gain control. Move the probe to pin 1 of the same tube. If the noise is not heard, it is coming from the V603 stage. Keep touching the probe successively to the input or output of the various stages, working toward the gain control.
- **Stage Blocking.** The signal tracing method just described can be used with the signal tracer in the audio circuits only. If a signal tracer containing tuned circuits and a demodulator is available, it can be used in the rf and i-f sections. A simpler and quicker method is stage blocking, which is similar to that

used in troubleshooting hum defects. It can be used also in the audio section. Connect a clip to a test lead and fasten the clip to a convenient point on the chassis. Turn the gain control R105 so the noise can be heard with good volume. Touch the lead to the grid (pin 1) of V603. If the noise continues, it is in the V603 stage. If the noise stops, it is between pin 1 of V603 and the antenna. Touch the probe successively to the control grids of the various stages, working toward the antenna. If the noise continues when a point is shorted out, the noise is originating between that point and the last point that was shorted out. If the noise stops when a point is shorted out, the noise is originating between that point and the antenna.

TROUBLESHOOTING A RECEIVER THAT SQUEALS OR MOTORBOATS

Squealing and motorboating are terms sometimes used to describe unwanted sounds or noises in the output of receivers. Very low-frequency sounds are classified as motorboating because they sound like the "put-put" of a motorboat. Motorboating is usually the result of a component failure in the audio section of the receiver that produces regenerative feedback in the audio amplifiers. Squealing may be produced by anything that causes regenerative feedback in any of the amplifier stages of the receiver; however, it is sometimes produced by interfering radio signals. Disconnect the antenna and short-circuit the antenna terminals to determine whether the squeal is caused by external interfering signals or internal troubles. If the squealing stops with the antenna disconnected, the trouble is usually external.

Squealing Caused by Internal Conditions

The squealing sounds described in this section are high-pitched audio sounds. They are usually caused by unwanted oscillations in one or more stages of the rf or i-f section of the receiver. Squealing may originate also in the audio section. In either case, the squealing is the result of unwanted oscillations. The difference is that the oscillations, if in the audio circuits, would occur at the same frequency as the squealing sounds. While in the rf or i-f circuit the oscillations would occur at or near the frequency to which the circuits are tuned. The audible squealing sound is then produced by the heterodyning of two or more frequencies of unwanted oscillations with each other, or the unwanted oscillations with a received signal.

Causes of Unwanted Oscillations

The causes of unwanted oscillations are many but they have one thing in common. They each produce regeneration. Component failure in decoupling filters sometimes causes regeneration. If the capacitor becomes open or reduced in value or the resistor changes to a lower value, the filtering action is reduced and signal variations will occur in the voltage that was previously decoupled by the filter. These decoupling filters are used in DC voltage sources, such as AVC, AGC, plate, screen and bias supplies that are common to two or more stages of amplification. Poor shielding, a tube shield left off its tube after replacing the tube, or lead dress not being restored to its original condition after replacing a component, are all causes of undesirable coupling that may be regenerative and cause unwanted oscillations.

Sectionalizing Source of Oscillations

- **Audio Signal Tracing.** Refer to Fig. 6-1. If the oscillating condition is present whether a signal is tuned in or not, and does not vary when the set is tuned, it probably is originating in the audio section. The audio section includes the detector through the audio output V603. Turn the gain control R105 to the extreme counterclockwise (off) position. If the squeal stops, it is originating between the gain control and the detector. If the squeal continues, it is originating between the gain control and the audio output terminals.
- **RF Signal Tracing.** If the squealing is present only after a signal is tuned in, and it is heard with all signals, the oscillation is most likely in the rf section. It would likely be between the first i-f amplifier and the detector. If the squeal is heard only when the set is receiving a signal and it occurs mostly at one end of a tuning stage, the rf amplifier is probably at fault.

Localizing Squeal or Motorboating

The stage blocking method just described can be used. If the trouble is thought to be in the audio section, short out the detector. If the squeal stops, the trouble is between the antenna and the detector; if it continues, it is between the detector and the audio output. The shorting probe can be moved to any of the audio tube grid terminals. Whenever a point is found where the squeal stops, the

130

Table 6-2. Typical Capacitor, Resistor, and Inductor Failures in a Receiver Stage

Symptoms	DC Voltage Measurements	Resistance Measurements	Defective Part
			Plate bypass capacitor.
1. Feedback or hum	a. Normal.	a. Capacitor does not charge*.	a Open
No output or very weak signal	b. Zero or very low from plate to ground	b. Partial or direct short from the B+ line to ground	b. Shorted Screen bypass capacitor.
2. Decreased output and motor-boating	a. Normal	a. Capacitor does not charge *	a. Open
No output or very weak output. Hot screen resistor.	b. Zero or very low from screen to ground.	b Partial or direct short from screen to ground	b. Shorted
3. Weak output	a. Normal	a. Capacitor does not charge*	a. Open
Distorted output	b. No reading across capacitor	b Partial or direct short from cathode to ground	b. Shorted
			Coupling capacitor.
4. No output or weak output	a. Normal	a. Capacitor does not charge*	A. Open
Distorted output	b. High reading from grid to ground. Positive polarity at grid	b. Low reading across caoupling capacitor	b. Shorted
			Series grid resistor. coil or secondary winding.
5. Severe hum or blocking	a. No reading across component part	a. Open circuit reading from grid to ground or to bias line	a. Open
No output or very weak output.	b. No reading across component part	b. Partial or direct short from grid to ground or to bias line	b. Shorted
			Series plate resistor. coil. or primary winding
6. No output or very weak output	a. no reading from plate to ground	a. No reading from plate to B+ line	a. Open
No output or very weak output	b. High reading from plate to ground	b Partial or direct short from plate to B+line	b. Shorted coil
7. No output or very weak output	High reading across resistor	Open circuit reading across terminals of resistor*	Cathode resistor Open
8. No output or very weak output	No reading from screen grid to ground	Open circuit reading from screen grid 'o B+ line	Screen-grid dropping resistor open

Test to be made with one end of part detached from circuit

squeal is originating ahead of that point. It is possible for the squeal to be caused by troubles in two stages. Therefore, if the trouble is corrected in one faulty stage, and it still squeals, another stage nearby may also be handled by removing tubes one at a time. Remove the af amplifier V602A. If the squeal stops, the trouble is originating between this stage and the detector. If the squeal does not stop, it is originating between this stage and the output.

UNIVERSAL TROUBLESHOOTING CHART

The receiver troubleshooting chart in Table 6-2 will be of assistance in locating troubles quickly. The information is general and can be applied to any receiver. You can get an idea as to what the trouble is, regardless of the model.

Chapter 7
Repairing Radio Parts

Fix up, patch up and make do! That was the motto of the 1930s, the time when many of the collectible radios were made. In the Great Depression of the 1930s, radios and radio parts were available—if you had the money to buy them. Now radios like the old-time radios are no longer made, so tubes and other parts for them are obsolete and hard to come by. This is the major problem of the collector or restorer of old-time radios—the unavailability of replacement parts. Fortunately there are ways around this problem. One solution is to repair parts rather than replace them. In the case of tubes, of course, repair is not possible, but substitution is. Often it is possible to replace one old-time tube with another of the same vintage. This chapter will show you how to make do with the original parts of your old-time radio by repairing or rebuilding them. The next chapter will complete the picture by showing how to substitute for parts you cannot buy or repair.

REPAIRS IN GENERAL

Radio repair is the work done to restore a radio set to efficient operating condition after troubleshooting has identified and isolated the fault. It consists of realignment, the replacement of defective parts—including tubes—and all necessary disassembly and reassembly work.

When unsoldering a connection, whether it is the pig-tailed lead of a resistor or capacitor, or the lead of a transformer, heat the solder joint just enough to melt the solder. When the solder is soft, use a tool to separate the lead from the lug (Fig. 7-1). Twisting and pulling at the lead can splatter solder into inaccessible places and cause short circuits that are difficult to find, and can break the connecting lug. Shake excess solder from the iron to prevent the solder from dropping into the set.

When a part is being replaced, tag the disconnected leads or identify them in a sketch to insure proper connections to the new part (Fig. 7-2).

INSTALLING SMALL REPLACEMENT PARTS

When defective parts are replaced, exact replacement parts must be used if available. This procedure will insure normal operation of the radio if it operated normally before the part failed. If an exact replacement part is not available, and the original part is beyond repair, an equivalent or better part should be substituted for it.

The new part must, if at all possible, be installed in the same place. If this is out of the question, and there is room elsewhere, it

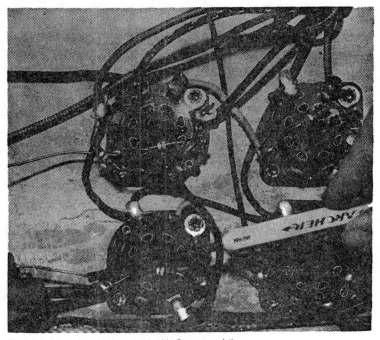

Fig. 7-1. Use of soldering tool with 2-pronged tip.

Fig. 7-2. Tags identifying wires from chassis and corresponding terminals on the large loop antenna of a Sparton console.

can be installed where there is space. The disadvantage in changing the position of parts, especially in rf units or other high-frequency circuits, is that the change may effect the tuning and alignment.

Before soldering any connections, carefully scrape and clean all connections on parts that will come in contact with solder. This means removing all corrosion, paint and also the enamel insulation of the wire leads. Tin the lugs and leads with solder to be sure that when the joint is made there will be a perfect bond by the solder. Make a good mechanical connection by twisting the wire lead around the lug several times before soldering. Do not depend on the solder to form a mechanical bond. Use only enough solder to join the wire to the lug and remove the soldering iron as soon as solder flows well into the joint. When soldering very small parts such as low-wattage resistors, ceramic capacitors, or germanium diodes, hold the pig-tailed lead with a pair of long-nosed pliers at a point between the part and the joint you are about to solder. Thus interposed between the part and the source of heat, the pliers form a sink into which the excessive heat drains off before reaching the part. Hold the pliers in this position until after the solder has cooled. This quickens the cooling of the solder while at the same time it continues to protect the part against the heat.

REPAIR AND REPLACEMENT OF VARIABLE CAPACITORS

Variable capacitors do not normally become defective during operation. Mishandling a receiver can ruin capacitor plates or bend them out of place; it may then be necessary to replace the capacitor or capacitor gang. If the plates are bent only slightly they can be straightened out with ordinary tools. Other troubles include poor contact at the rotor wiper springs, and loose "pig-tail" connections.

A receiver can become erratic if there is dirt or other foreign matter between the tuning capacitor plates. The trouble will be

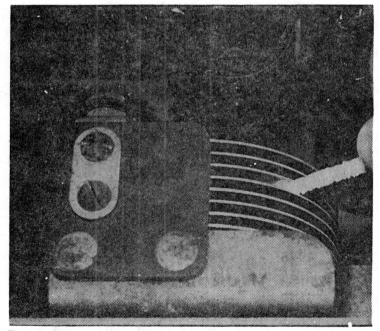

Fig. 7-3. Use a pipe cleaner to clear away dirt and plating slivers from plates of a tuning capacitor.

135

noticed mostly while the set is being tuned. The spaces between the plates can be cleaned with an ordinary pipe cleaner (Fig. 7-3).

Some receiver tuning capacitor plates are plated with zinc or other metallic material. The plating may peel over small areas and leave slivers that will cause arcing or erratic operation. If the plates have wide spacing between them, the plating can be removed with a pair of long-nosed pliers.

If the slivers cannot be removed, they can be burned off by connecting a high AC voltage across the capacitor. Sometimes the line voltage will be sufficient. If not, the high voltage may be obtained from the high-voltage winding of a separate power transformer. If a separate transformer is not available, it can be taken from the high-voltage winding of the transformer of the set under repair. For safety, a light bulb should be connected in series with the AC line voltage. The coil connected across the capacitor must be disconnected to prevent it from burning out. To prevent any possible damage to the filter circuit, the rectifier should be removed, if the set transformer is used.

If the capacitor develops trouble, every effort should be made to repair it, rather than replace it, for replacement would involve realignment of the rf, mixer and local oscillator. If the capacitor cannot be repaired, the replacement work will be difficult.

REPAIRING AND CLEANING ELECTRICAL CONTACTS

The spacing between the electrical contacts in switches is often critical. If the troubleshooter finds they are touching when they should not be touching, or vice versa, the contacts must be set to their proper positions. Sometimes this involves the bending of a wiper. Wipers and other spring contacts can be bent only a few times before they fatigue and break, and a new unit must be installed.

Use an abrasive, such as a fine emery cloth, to clean the contacts when possible.

TUBE SOCKET REPAIR

When the body of a socket is defective, it must be replaced. The defective socket cannot be repaired. Certain types of sockets, especially octals, have replaceable contacts.

When a tube is removed from a socket by rocking it from side to side, one or more of the metal contact sleeves within the tube socket might become spread. This may result in poor or intermittent contact between the tube pin and the metal sleeve when a tube is reinserted in the socket. The metal sleeve of the contact may be repaired by inserting the tip of a pair of long-nosed pliers into the tube socket hole and compressing the sleeve to its original shape. If long-nosed pliers do not fit into the tube socket hole, insert a pointed tool such as an awl between the sleeve and the inside wall of the hole containing it.

If the terminal is merely bent out of shape so that contact cannot be made or is intermittent, it probably can be bent back into shape with a pair of long-nosed pliers. It might also be possible to make contact by inserting a pointed tool, such as an awl, between the contact and socket body.

CORD AND CABLE REPAIRS

Cord trouble results from the breakage of a conductor at the connecting plug. To make the indicated repairs.

—Thread the cord through the hole in the plug and tie the wires in a simple knot. This procedure will keep the strain on the knot, rather than on the connection (Fig. 7-4).

—Remove about one-half inch of the insulation from the end of each conductor and tin the ends of the wires. The tinning will form a solid mass at the ends and will eliminate loose ends and possible short circuits.

—Wrap each wire in a clockwise direction around a prong, then around a screw. When the screw is tightened, the wire will be pulled tight in the same direction (Fig. 7-5).

In multiconductor cables the most common trouble is a broken

Fig. 7-4. The wires of a line cord have been threaded through a plug and tied to provide a strain relief.

conductor at the connector terminal. To effect repairs.

—Remove the broken end from the terminal while heating it with a soldering iron.

—If the remaining wire is too short to reach the terminal, splice and solder a piece to it as an extension. Slip a piece of spaghetti tubing over the wire before the splice is made. After splicing and soldering, slide the spaghetti tubing over the joint.

—Solder the other end of the extension to the proper terminal. If necessary, clean out the excess solder from the terminal by heating it with a soldering iron. Shake out the old solder while it is still hot. All the conductors should be inspected, because if one is broken, others may be broken, or be near the breaking point. If others are badly worn, replace the entire cable.

REPAIRING SHIELDED CABLES AND WIRES

Shielded cables are repaired in the same manner as unshielded cables. The purpose of the shielding is to keep magnetic fields from causing interference in the cable and to prevent radiation from reaching the conductors. It is therefore important to reconnect the shield if it has been disconnected.

If the shielded cable has only one conductor in addition to the shield, the shield should always bear the strain. This is accomplished by making the shield connection shorter than any other connection, so that the shield will prevent the other conductor from breaking when any strain is put on the cable.

REPAIRING TRANSFORMER WINDINGS

If a primary or secondary winding is open, repair is impossible except in a relatively few cases. Such cases occur when the open winding is on the outside—that is, when it appears on top of the other windings—and when the break is on the surface layer and not buried under one or more turns of wire.

Repairable breaks are those that occur where a lead is soldered to the thin wire of a winding. The cause of the break, most often, is corrosion. Repair is effected by resoldering.

In a few instances, it may be possible to repair a break inside a winding (below the surface layer) by fusion. Such a repair, however, would be only temporary. It is effected by applying a high voltage momentarily across the ends of the winding; the power used should be of several hundred volts taken from the B+ line. If the separation is not too great, the applied voltage may cause an arc that will fuse the separated ends of the wire.

Fig. 7-5. The wires have been attached to the plug screws in the proper manner.

TUBE REACTIVATION

If a tube checker indicates that a tube has low emission, it may be possible to reactivate the tube. Apply a voltage of two to three times the normal voltage to the filaments for a few seconds with the plate voltage removed. This will force to the surface some of the electrons that are well within the cathode. This procedure is a temporary one and applies only to tubes with certain types of cathode material. However, it can be tried on any tube if the tube cannot be used otherwise.

If the tube does not respond to this treatment, the filament can be subjected to a voltage about 1½ times the normal value for several hours with the plate voltage removed.

REWINDING RF COILS AND CHOKES

Most rf coils and chokes used in old radios can be easily wound by hand, or with a lathe or drill press. If the wire on the defective coil has been damaged by corrosion, it is only necessary to remove and count the number of turns of wire originally on the coil. Clean the

139

form thoroughly and rewind the coil with new wire, using the same size wire and number of turns as before.

In instances where it is necessary to construct the entire coil, select the proper diameter form. Unless a close wound winding is definitely specified, the number of turns of wire should be spaced to fill the required length on the form. The length specified should be marked on the form and holes drilled opposite the pins to which the ends of the winding are to connect. Scrape one end of the wire and pass it through the lower hole in the form to the pin to which the bottom end of the winding will connect and solder this end. Unroll an amount of wire sufficient to make the winding and clamp the spool in a vise so it will not turn. The wire should be pulled out straight and the winding started by turning the form in the hands and walking up toward the vise. A fair tension should be kept on the wire at all times. The spacing can be judged by the eye. If, as the winding progresses, it becomes evident that the spacing is going to be incorrect to fill the required length, the winding can be started over again with a different spacing. If the spacing is only slightly off, the winding can be completed, the top end fastened, and the spacing corrected by pushing each turn. After a little practice, it will be difficult to determine the correct spacing.

Another efficient method of winding coils is with a drill press or lathe, operating at a slow speed. A mechanical counting device attached to the drill press or lathe makes this method particularly useful in accurately winding chokes and coils containing many turns of wire.

REPAIRING SWITCHES

Multicontact switches should be cleaned with solvent and a brush. After the switch has been cleaned, a careful inspection should be made of the spring tension for each contact, and the tension increased on any weak contacts. The tension on wave-band switch contacts can be increased by carefully bending the contact slightly with a small hook shaped bending tool, as shown in Figure 7-5.

REPAIRING FIXED VARIABLE RESISTORS

When a carbon resistor becomes overheated, its resistance decreases. The resistance may be raised to the correct value simply by scrapping part of the carbon from the body until the correct value is obtained. A wire-wound resistor can sometimes be repaired by

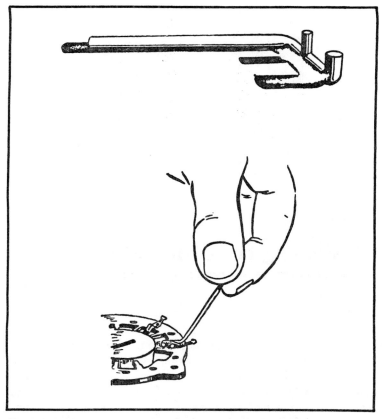

Fig. 7-6. Suggested way for increasing switch-contact tension.

placing a clamp over the break or by shorting the break. This restores continuity with a slight decrease in resistance.

Variable resistors and potentiometers, as used in volume controls, seldom burn out, because of the small amount of current that passes through them. Faulty operation is generally due to poor contact, wear and dirt at the rubbing contacts. Clean these thoroughly with solvent. Polish them with an ordinary pencil eraser, one which is not too gritty, and adjust the tension of the arm so that it makes a firm contact. If the variable resistor is too worn to make a temporary repair, replace it with a fixed resistor, the value of which must be found by experimentation. If the variable resistor is wire wound and there is a break in the winding, slipping a small metal tab underneath the broken section will restore continuity in most instances.

Chapter 8
Substituting For Unavailable Parts

In restoring old-time radios, we are often confronted with a dilemma. One part of the dilemma is the unavailability of replacement parts. The other part is the impossibility or impracticality of repairing some parts. The solution is substitution. Substitution is particularly applicable to tubes, which cannot be repaired. The information in this chapter shows which tubes can be replaced by which other tubes and what changes—if any—must be made to circuit wiring to accommodate the replacements. The chapter includes a *Mini-Manual of Old-Time Tubes*, which will allow you to compare old-time tubes to see which are interchangeable. The chapter also includes much other information about substituting for tubes and other parts.

TUBE SUBSTITUTION

If a tube is not available to replace one that is defective, a substitute must be used. However, the equipment probably will not operate as well as it did with the original tube and considerable labor may be involved. Do not put a substitute tube into a socket unless the substitute tube characteristics and socket connections have been compared with those of the original tube (refer to the *Mini-Manual of Old-Time Tubes*), If this procedure is not followed, the filaments may burn out or the power supply may be short-circuited.

A tube of similar electrical characteristics may prove a more or less effective substitute depending upon the purpose for which it would be used. A power tube would not be used to replace a voltage amplifier because the filament and plate current drain (see *Mini-Manual*) would probably be excessive. If the tubes are wired in parallel, a slight difference in filament current rating will not matter. If the filaments are in series, the filament drain must be the same for all tubes.

A tube of similar electrical characteristics may be physically different from the original tube. If it is considerably larger, it may not be usable. If it has a different type of base (see *Mini Manual*), the socket will have to be changed to make it available for use.

Tube substitution in critical rf amplifier and oscillator circuits may necessitate the realignment of the circuits.

Table 8-1 is a ready reference of the tube substitutions that I have found easiest and most likely to succeed. In each case, the substitute tube fits the same socket as the original tube and takes the same filament voltage. No wiring changes are required, but there may be some differences in gain, internal capacitances, filament *current* and other characteristics. In going from a metal to a glass tube, you may have to install a shielding can on the glass replacement tube.

For more information about tube substitutions, refer to the sections Data and Uses of the Tube Manual and Use of the Mini-Manual or Old-Time Tubes.

DATA AND USES OF THE TUBE MANUAL

Information in the tube manual is often helpful to the radio restorer. Suppose, for example, you have a defective 6A7 type tube for which you must find a substitute. There is no direct substitution possible for this tube, so it is not listed in Table 8-1. However, the *RCA Receiving Tube Manual* excerpt in Appendix A shows that the type 6A8 is electrically equivalent to the 6A7 and requires only the replacement of the 7-prong socket with an 8-prong socket.

USE OF THE MINI-MANUAL OF OLD/TIME TUBES

The *Mini-Manual of Old-Time Tubes,* incorporated in this volume as a book within a book, is a guide to the tubes used in old-time radios, As such, it is a unique aid to the restorer or collector of old-time radios. The *Mini-Manual* will allow you to compare the various old tubes to determine which are interchangeable and what wiring changes are required. (Table 8-1 shows the substitutions for which no wiring changes are required.)

Table 8-1. Ready reference of easiest and most successful tube substitutions.

Original Tube	Replacements for Original Tube
27	56
37	76
41	42
42	41
56	27
75	77, 78, 6D6
76	37
77	75, 78, 6D6
78	75, 77, 6D6
80	83, 5Z3
3P5	3C5, 3Q5
3C5	3B5, 3Q5
3Q5	3E5, 3C5
5Z3	80, 83
6AF6	6N6
6AX5	6W5, 6X5
6B6	6Q7, 6R7, 6T7, 6V7
6D6	75, 77 ,78
6J5	6L5, 6P5
6J7	6K7, 6S7, 6U7, 6W7
6K6	6V6
6K7	6J7, 6S7, 6U7, 6W7
6L5	6J5, 6P5
6N6	6AB6
6P5	6J5, 6I5
6Q7	6B6, 6R7, 6T7, 6V7
6R7	6B6, 6Q7, 6T7, 6V7
6S7	6J7, 6K7, 6U7, 6W7
6T7	6B6, 6Q7, 6R7, 6V7
6U7	6J7, 6K7, 6S7, 6W7
6V7	6B6, 6Q7, 6R7, 6T7
6X5	6AX5, 6W5
6W5	6AX5, 6X5
6W7	6J7, 6K7, 6S7, 6U7
25A6	25B6, 25C6, 25L6
25B6	25A6, 25C6, 25L6
25L6	25A6, 25B6, 25C6
25Y5	25Z5
25Z5	25Y5
50C6	50L6
50L6	50C6

The first thing to look for in determing interchangeability is whether the tubes have the same base connections. Figure 8-1 shows the base diagrams for the various tubes in the *Mini-Manual*. In the *Mini-Manual* the type of base is indicated by two figures, which are keyed to the drawings in Fig. 8-1.

In some AC-DC sets, the filaments are wired in series. There is no transformer to drop the line voltage to the filament voltage.

Instead, the filaments and a series resistor are connected directly across the AC line. For this scheme to work, a substitute tube must have approximately the same cathode current (filament drain) as the original tube. Even with some transformer-powered AC radios in which the filaments are in parallel, the filament current drain may

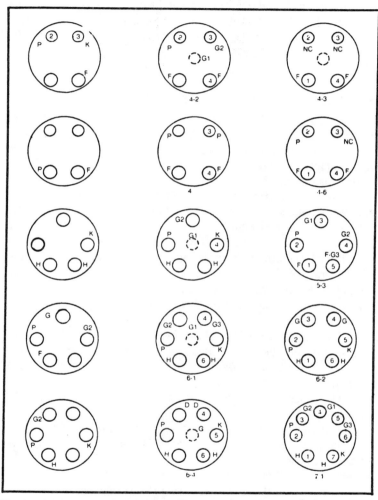

Fig. 8-1 Base connections of old-time tubes, looking from the bottom of the tube. Sketch references such as 4-1 are referred to in Base column of the Mini-Manual of Old-Time Tubes. Small centered circles drawn in dashed lines denote plate cap or grid cap. Electrode symbols are: D, diode plate; F, filament; G, grid; G1, inner grid; G2, screen grid; G3, suppressor grid; H, heater; K, cathode; NC, no connection; P, plate.

145

prevent some tubes from being used as substitutes, because the current drain may be more than the transformer can handle.

The voltages of other elements are not as critical as the filament voltage, but improper plate, screen or grid voltage can cause weak or distorted reception. Excessive plate current drain can overload the transformer, and can also cause immediate or premature failure of the tube or other parts. Insufficient grid bias (not negative enough) can cause excessive plate current, as can using a tube with too high a rated plate current.

SUBSTITUTE FILAMENT AND PLATE TRANSFORMERS

If a transformer is defective and an exact replacement is not available, a similar transformer may be used if its electrical characteristics and connections are known. Such information can be found by using an ohmmeter and AC voltmeter. The ohmmeter and voltmeter may be combined in a multimeter or VTVM.

If the proposed substitute is too large to be installed in the space that was occupied by the original transformer, it may, in an extreme emergency, be connected externally. You must also determine whether the replacement transformer has the proper power rating.

Most transformers have terminals which are usually numbered. If a diagram of the windings and terminals appears on the transformer, the identification will be simple. If there is no diagram, the windings can be identified by their resistances and voltage tests described below.

Some transformers have leads instead of terminals. If the leads are color coded, they can be identified by comparing the colors with those in Table 8-2. Although this code is standard, other codes pertain in some cases.

The windings on the transformer with leads can be identified by visual inspection and by the thickness of the leads. The thicker leads are from the filament winding because the filaments draw more current than other circuits. In some transformers, there will be two or three filament windings: one for the rectifier filaments and the others for the other filaments. The rectifier filament usually draws less current than the other tube filaments combined.

The high-voltage winding carries the least amount of current, so the leads to it will be the thinnest of all. The primary winding is also thin; the difference can be determined by resistance measurements. Connect one ohmmeter prod to one lead and check for continuity to all other leads one at a time. The high-voltage winding

146

Table 8-2. Power-Transformer-Lead Color Code.

Leads	Colors
Primary	Black
If tapped:	
Common	Black
Tap	Black and yellow stripes
Finish	Black and red stripes
High-voltage plate	Red
Center tap	Red and yellow stripes
Rectifier filament	Yellow
Center tap	Yellow and blue stripes
Filament No. 1	Green
Center tap	Green and yellow stripes
Filament No. 2	Brown
Center tap	Brown and yellow stripes
Filament No. 3	Slate
Center tap	Slate and yellow stripes

will have the highest resistance, and the primary winding will have the next highest resistance.

A further check can be made with an AC voltmeter. When the primary winding has been found by the tests described above, connect it to the AC power line. Set the voltmeter to the highest range and measure the voltage across the thinnest leads. There probably will be three wires; the third one is the center tap in the case of a full-wave rectifier circuit. The highest voltage will appear across the ends of the winding. If one-half of this value is measured between either one of the end leads and another lead, the other lead is the center tap. The filament windings will show about 5 or 6 volts, depending on whether the winding being measured is the rectifier filament or the other filament winding.

There are some rectifier filaments that require 6.3 volts, rather than 5 volts. In this instance the winding with the thinner wire usually is the rectifier filament winding. If they are about the same size, and a low-reading ohmmeter does not show any difference, the leads with the heavier insulation feed the rectifier filaments. This is because this winding is usually at a high potential with respect to the chassis.

Some power transformers have thin leads in addition to the leads described above. They are probably taps on the primary winding. Such taps are provided so that the proper secondary voltages will be produced regardless of the line voltage. Continuity checks will show whether they are connected to the primary end leads. The highest resistance will be indicated between the extreme ends of the primary winding; the next highest reading will be indicated between the next highest voltage tap and the other end. If in doubt about which taps to use, connect the lead that indicates a high resistance to all the other taps to one side of the line, and one of the taps to the other side of the line. Measure the filament voltage under load. If it reads too high or too low, select another tap until the reading is about right. As long as the line voltage remains fixed around the same value, the connections can be made permanent.

Filament and plate transformers are treated the same as power transformers. There are only two windings, the primary and secondary. Some transformers of this type may have center-tapped secondaries. The filament leads will be much heavier than the primary leads. In a plate transformer, the high-voltage winding will have a greater resistance than the primary winding.

Figure 8-2 summarizes the color-code information about power transformers and also shows the color codes for i-f and interstage audio transformers. It also shows the colors that are sometimes used in chassis wiring for the purpose of circuit indentification. These standards are not always adhered to, especially in the older sets.

SUBSTITUTE FOR BALLAST OR LINE CORD RESISTOR

Back in the early 1930s, probably because of the Great Depression, the hard-pressed radio manufacturers sought a way to reduce the cost of their radios so that more people could afford them. They hit upon the idea of eliminating the expensive power transformer by connecting the tube filaments in series, directly across the AC line (Fig. 8-3). Of course, anything that is connected across the AC line has to drop (have a voltage rating of) 115 volts. To help drop the 115 volts, tube manufacturers brought out tubes with filaments rated at 25 volts or higher. A typical tube lineup in such sets was as follows: 6A8, 6K7, 6H6, 6F5, 25A6 and 25Z6. The filament voltages accounted for 74 volts of the 115-volt line voltage ($6 + 6 + 6 + 6 + 25 + 25 = 74$). This left 41 volts ($115 - 74 = 41$) to account for. To drop the 41 volts, the manufacturers added a resistance in series with the filaments to take care of the 41 volts. This resistance sometimes took the form of a length of heater wire enclosed in a glass bulb that was mounted on a tube base. These *ballast tubes,* as they were called, so resembled regular receiving tubes that some manufacturers couldn't resist the temptation to include them in the tube count for advertising. Some "8-tube" sets actually had only five operating tubes plus three ballast tubes. Interestingly, this practice of exaggerating the tube count had a sequel in the early days of transistor radios when transistors used as diodes were sometimes included in the transistor count.

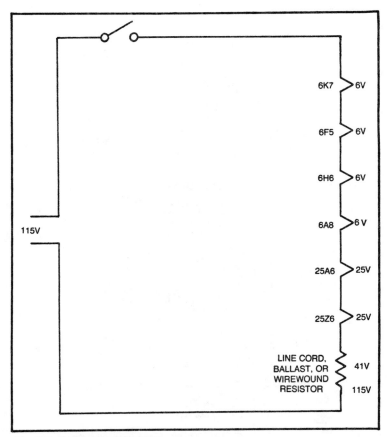

Fig. 8-3. Series tube filaments.

Sometimes the voltage-dropping resistance wire was enclosed within the line cord of the receiver (Fig. 8-4). Usually it was wound around an asbestos rope and covered with an insulating sheath. Then it was combined with the other two wires inside a rubber sheath, which was in turn covered with a woven cotton sheath. These resistance cords ran very warm and deteriorated faster than ordinary cords.

The radio restorer is often faced with the necessity of substituting for a nonavailable resistance cord or ballast tube. To do so requires a resistor of the proper resistance to drop the voltage in excess of that required by the filaments. The resistor must have sufficient power-handling capability to dissipate the heat generated by the current that will flow in it.

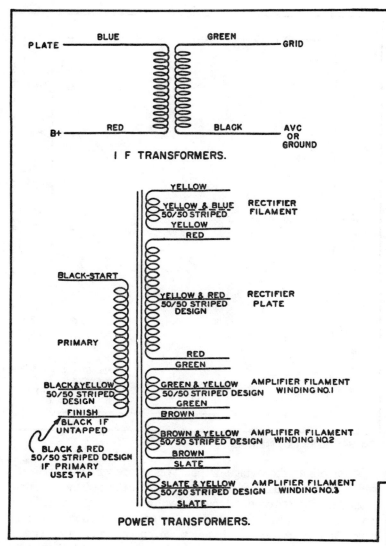

Fig. 8-2. Color code for transformers.

To calculate the resistance, begin by adding all the filament voltages. In the example, they total 74 volts. Next, subtract this from the live voltage (115 volts) to determine the amount that must be dropped by the voltage-dropping resistor. In this case, 41 volts must be dropped by the resistor. The next step is to determine the filament current of the tubes, which the tube manual (see Appendix

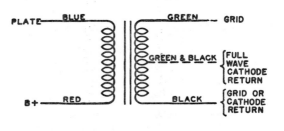

INTERSTAGE AUDIO
TRANSFORMERS

STANDARD COLORS USED IN CHASSIS WIRING FOR THE
PURPOSE OF CIRCUIT IDENTIFICATION OF THE EQUIPMENT
ARE AS FOLLOWS:

CIRCUIT	COLOR
GROUNDS, GROUNDED ELEMENTS, AND RETURNS...............................	BLACK.
HEATERS OR FILAMENTS, OFF GROUND..	BROWN.
POWER SUPPLY B PLUS.......................	RED.
SCREEN GRIDS......................................	ORANGE.
CATHODES...	YELLOW.
CONTROL GRIDS..................................	GREEN.
PLATES..	BLUE
POWER SUPPLY, MINUS.......................	VIOLET (PURPLE).
A C POWER LINES..................................	GRAY.
MISCELLANEOUS, ABOVE OR BELOW GROUND RETURNS, A V C, ETC..........	WHITE.

B) shows is 0.3 ampere. Now you have enough information to find
the resistance, which by Ohm's law is the voltage (41 volts) divided
by the current (0.3 ampere). This is calculated as follows:

$$R = \frac{\text{volts}}{\text{amperes}} = \frac{41}{0.3} = 137 \text{ ohms (approximately)}$$

The nearest standard resistance value is 150 ohms.

To calculate the required power rating for the resistor, again
use the voltage and current determined above; only this time,
multiply instead of divide.

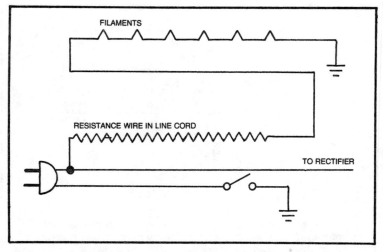

Fig. 8-4. The old sets often had a length of resistance wire in the line cord. These resistance cords are often defective.

P = volts × amperes = 41 × 0.3 = 12 watts (approximately)
There are 12-watt resistors available, but a better choice would be 15, 20, or 25 watts. A larger power rating provides a safety factor. A 150-ohm, 20-watt Ohmite *Brown Devil* would work fine. Be sure to mount the resistor away from cabinet and circuit parts susceptible to heat damage.

LOUDSPEAKER

The old-time sets generally used a large electrodynamic speaker with a field coil winding that was in series with the plate voltage. Figure 8-5 shows the connections of this type of speaker. Because the field coil was in series with the plate supply, it acted as the filter choke of the supply. Since the field coil was matched to the other components in the power supply, it is best to repair the speaker, rather than replace it.

Another type of speaker is found in some radios, especially newer ones. This is the permanent magnet type, illustrated in Fig. 8-6. In these a permanent magnet takes the place of the field coil and electromagnet. Chokes are available from electronic supply stores and mail order houses. The choke you select should have an inductance of 7 henrys or so at 100-200 milliamperes.

It is sometimes possible to repair loudspeakers. A tear in the paper cone of a speaker is usually repairable with a small piece of

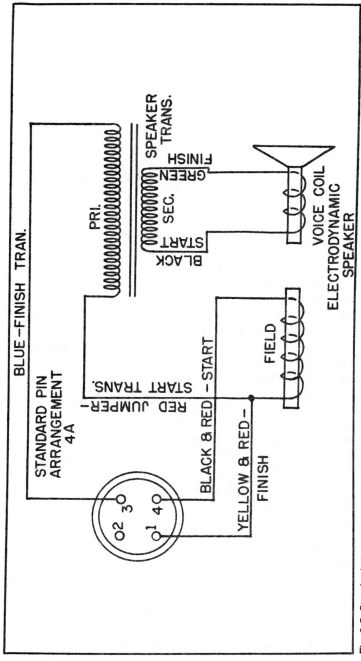

Fig. 8-5. Standard pin arrangement and color code for electrodynamic speakers, which were used in the earliest speaker-equipped radios.

153

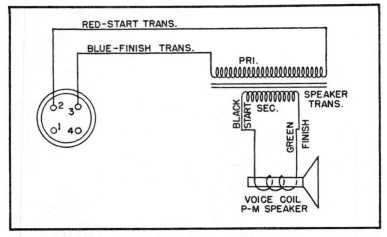

Fig. 8-6. Standard pin arrangement and color code for permanent magnet speakers used in some sets.

masking tape. Be careful you don't make the tear worse, as old speaker cones usually become brittle with age.

Occasionally the voice coil of a speaker will rub against the pole piece of the magnet, causing rattles and distortion. Usually you can recenter the voice coil and stop the rubbing.

In testing an old speaker, note that the field coils of old speakers will read 500-2000 ohms on an ohmmeter, and voice coils 8 ohms. Recently made speakers may read 3-6 ohms. New headphones may read either a very low resistance (3-6 ohms for dynamic speaker types) or a very high impedance (almost infinity for crystal types). These new speakers and headphones are not suitable for use with old radios designed for a headphone resistance of 1000-2000 ohms. It is possible to match one of the new low-impedance speakers to the plate resistance of the audio output of an old radio by using a new audio transformer. The secondary impedance of the audio transformer should be the same as the voice coil impedance (3-4 ohms in some new speakers, 6-8 ohms in others). The primary impedance of the transformer should approximate the load resistance (impedance) of the audio output tube (last audio tube). Look up the load resistance in the *Mini Manual* or in the tube characteristics section of Appendix B.

SUBSTITUTE RESISTORS AND CAPACITORS

In some instances a resistor or capacitor of a certain value may not be obtainable and a substitute part must be used. An application of Ohm's law will quickly determine the correct value of resistors or capacitors that can be used in series or parallel to replace the original part. For example, if a 1000-ohm, 2-watt resistor is required but not obtainable, use two 500-ohm, 1-watt resistors in series, or two 2000-ohm, 1-watt resistors in parallel. In the case of capacitors, if a 1-UF, 400-volt capacitor is required, either two 2-UF, 200-volt capacitors in series can be used, or two 0.5-UF, 400-volt capacitors in parallel.

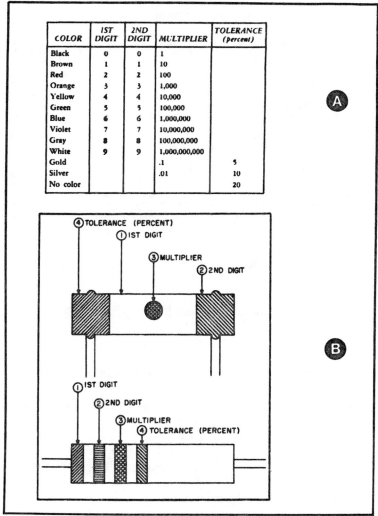

Fig. 8-7. Resistor color codes: body-end-dot (top) and bands (bottom).

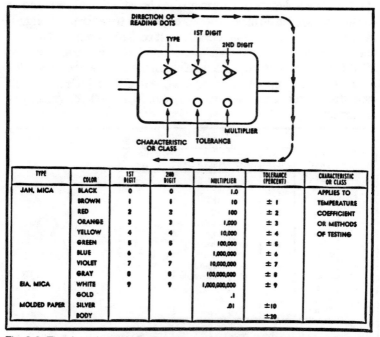

Fig. 8-8. The dot color code for the mica and molded paper capacitors found in old radios.

In general, the total resistance R_t of two resistors in series is given by

$$R_t = R_1 = R_2$$

The total resistance of two resistors in series is given by

$$R_t = \frac{R_1 + R_2}{R_1 \times R_2}$$

The total power rating of resistors in series or parallel is simply the sum of the individual ratings.

Capacitances in series add as do resistors in parallel; that is

$$C_t = \frac{C_1 + C_2}{C_1 \times C_2}$$

Capacitances in parallel add as do resistances in series; that is

$$C_t = C_1 + C_2$$

The voltage rating of capacitors in parallel is the same as that of the capacitor with the lowest voltage rating. The voltage rating of capacitors in series is the sum of the individual ratings.

Some of the resistors and capacitors used in the old-time radios are different from modern parts. To help you determine the electrical values of these parts, Fig. 8-7 through 8-11 give the color codes for the old parts (as well as new ones).

Figure 8-7 shows the markings on two types of resistors. Figure 8-8 presents the dot color code for the mica and molded paper capacitors that you find in the old sets. Figure 8-9 shows the 5-dot color code that was used on capacitors with various dielectrics. Figure 8-10 gives the 6-band color code for tubular paper dielectric capacitors. And Fig. 8-11 shows the color code for ceramic capacitors of various configurations. These figures should help you identify almost any resistor or capacitor that was marked according to some standard code.

MINI MANUAL OF OLD-TIME TUBES

The following table gives characteristics of various old radio tubes. The tubes are designated by number. Only the last two figures are required to identify the tube. For example, tube 301-A or 201-A appears in the table as 01-A. The type of base (illustrated in

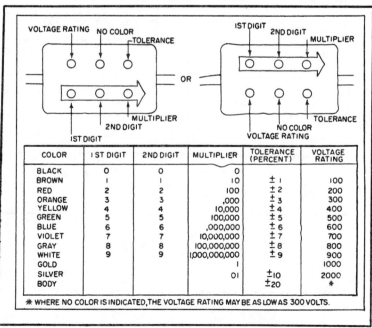

COLOR	I ST DIGIT	2ND DIGIT	MULTIPLIER	TOLERANCE (PERCENT)	VOLTAGE RATING
BLACK	0	0	0		
BROWN	1	1	10	± 1	100
RED	2	2	100	± 2	200
ORANGE	3	3	,000	± 3	300
YELLOW	4	4	10,000	± 4	400
GREEN	5	5	100,000	± 5	500
BLUE	6	6	,000,000	± 6	600
VIOLET	7	7	10,000,000	± 7	700
GRAY	8	8	100,000,000	± 8	800
WHITE	9	9	1,000,000,000	± 9	900
GOLD			1		1000
SILVER			01	±10	2000
BODY				±20	*

* WHERE NO COLOR IS INDICATED, THE VOLTAGE RATING MAY BE AS LOW AS 300 VOLTS.

Fig. 8-9. The five-dot color code that was once used on capacitors with various dielectrics.

CHARACTERISTICS OF THERMIONIC VACUUM TUBES

Type No	Purpose	Base	Cathode Type	Cathode Voltage	Cathode Current amp.	Plate voltage	Plate current mA	Screen voltage	Grid bias volts	Plate resist. ohms	Amp. factor	Mutual cond. μ umbo	Power output m watts	Load resist. ohms
00-A	Detector	4-1	Fil.	5.0	0.25	45	1.5		0	30000	20.0	666		
01-A	Gen. purpose	4-1	Fil.	5.0	0.25	90	2.5		4.5	11000	8.0	725		
11	Gen. purpose	4-1	Fil.	1.1	0.25	135	3.0		10.5	15000	6.6	440		
12	Gen. purpose	4-1	Fil.	1.1	0.25	135	3.0		10.5	15000	6.6	440		
12-A	Power output	4-1	Fil.	5.0	0.25	180	7.6		13.5	5000	8.5	1700	260	10800
20	R.F. amplifier	4-1	Fil.	3.3	0.13	135	6.5		22.5	6300	3.3	525	110	6500
22	R.F. amplifier	5-2	Heat	15.0	1.35	135	1.0	30	1.5	700000	400	570		
22	R.F. amplifier	4-2	Fil.	3.3	0.13	135	1.5	45	1.5	850000	350	300		
24-A	Amplifier	5-2	Heat	2.5	1.75	180	4.0	90	3.0	400000	400	1000		
26	Detector	4-1	Fil.	1.5	1.05	135	5.5		10.0	7600	8.3	1100		
26	Gen. purpose	5-1	Heat	15.0	0.35	90	4.5		1.5	9000	10.5	1165		
27	Gen. purpose	5-1	Heat	2.5	1.75	135	4.5		9.0	9000	9.0	1000		
28	Spec. det.	5-1	Heat	15.0	0.35	90	7.5		1.5	9000	10.5	1165		
29	Power amp	5-1	Heat	2.5	1.00	180	4.5		3.0	20700	30.0	1450	185	7000
30	Power amp	5-1	Heat	15.0	0.35	180	22.0		27.0	3500	3.8	1100	375	5700
30	Gen. purpose	4-1	Fil.	2.0	0.06	180	3.1		13.5	10300	9.3	900		
31	Power amp	4-1	Fil.	2.0	0.13	135	8.0		22.5	4100	3.8	925		
32	R.F. amplifier	4-2	Fil.	2.0	0.06	180	1.7	135	3.0	1.2meg	780	650		
32	Volt amplifier	5-1	Heat	15.0	0.35	135	1.5	67	13.5	32000	30.0	940	700	7000
33	Power amp	4-2	Fil.	2.0	0.26	135	14.5	90	3.0	50000	70.0	1450		
34	Variable-mu	4-2	Fil.	2.0	0.06	135	2.8	90	3.0	600000	360	600		
35	Variable-mu	5-2	Heat	2.5	1.75	250	6.5		3.0	350000	370	1050		
36	R.F. amplifier	5-2	Heat	6.3	0.30	180	3.1		3.0	350000	370	1050		
37	Gen. purpose	5-1	Heat	6.3	0.30	180	4.7		13.5	10000	9.0	900	525	13500
38	Power amp	5-2	Heat	6.3	0.30	135	9.0	135	13.5	102000	100	975		
39	Variable-mu	5-2	Heat	6.3	0.40	180	4.5	90	40.5	750000	750	1000		
40	Power amp	5-1	Heat	15.0	0.25	180	21.0		3.0	2000	3.0	1500		
40	Voltage amp	4-1	Fil.	5.0	0.65	180	0.2		3.0	150000	30	200		
41	Pow. pentode	6-3	Heat	6.3	0.65	167	16.5	167	12.5	120000	215	1800	1200	11000
42	Pow. pentode	6-3	Heat	6.3	0.30	250	34.0	250	16.5	100000	220	2200	3000	9000
43	Pow. pentode	6-3	Heat	25.0	0.30	95	20.0	95	15.0	45000	90	2000	900	4500
44	R.F. amplifier	5-2	Heat	6.30		90	6.0	90	3.0	150000	152	1010		
						180	6.4	90	3.0	410000	426	1040		
						250	6.5	90	3.0	600000	630	1050		

Type	Use	Base	Cathode	Fil. V	Fil. A	Plate V	Grid V	Screen V	Plate mA	Plate Res.	Amp. Factor	Gm	Power (mW)	Load
45	Power amp	4-1	Fil.	2.5	1.50	180	27.0		34.5	1900	3.5	1850	780	3500
46	Power amp	5-4	Fil.	2.5	1.75	250	34.0	250	50.0	1750	3.5	2000	1600	3900
						250	22.0	0	33.0	2380	5.6	2350	1250	6400
47	Power pentode	5-4	Fil.	2.5	1.75	250	4.0	0	0	60000	150	2400	16000	1300
48	Gen. purpose	5-1	Heat	15.0	0.35	300	6.0	95	0	60000	150	2500	20000	1450
48	Output tetrode	5-2	Heat	30.0	0.40	400	31.0		16.5	9000	10.5	1185	2500	7000
49	Power amp	5-3	Fil.	2.0	0.12	250	4.5	75	4.5	10000	28.0	2800	1600	
50	Power amp	4-1	Fil.	7.5	1.25	90	47.0	90	20.0	4000	4.5	1125	170	2000
51	Variable-mu	5-2	Fil.	2.5	1.75	95	5.7		20.0	1900	3.8	2000	2400	4100
						135	45.0		63.0	1800	3.8	2100	4600	4350
52	Output amp	4-1	Fil.	6.3	0.30	350	55.0		84.0	500000	525	1050		
55	Diode-triode	6-4	Heat	2.5	1.00	450	5.8		1.5	500000	525	1050		
56	Amplifier	5-1	Heat	2.5	1.00	180	6.3		3.0	7500	8.3	1100	1250	5000
56	Detector	5-1	Heat	2.5	1.00	250	42.0		20.0	9500	13.8	1450	20000	1500
57	R.F. amplifier	6-1	Heat	2.5	1.00	250	8.0	100	13.5	1.5 meg	13.8	1225	3000	7000
57	Detector	6-1	Heat	2.5	1.00	250	5.0	100	20.0					
58	A.F. amplifier	6-1	Heat	2.5	1.00	250	0.2	50	3.0	3 meg	1500	600	700	5350
58	Variable-mu	6-1	Heat	2.5	1.00	250	0.1	100	6.0	800000	1500	1600		
59	Three grid	6-1	Heat	2.5	1.00	250	0.5		1.0		1800	1200		
59	Power amp (As pentode)	7-1	Heat	2.5	2.00	250	8.2	250	3.0	2500	1280	2220	300	7000
64	R.F. amp	5-2	Heat	6.3	0.40	250	30.0	67	28.0	45000	6.0	1050	6000	2350
64	R.F. amp	5-2	Heat	6.3	0.40	400	15.0	67	0	350000	6.0	1000	1500	8000
67	Power amp	5-1	Heat	6.3	0.40	250	35.0		18.0	3200000	100	1100		
68	Output pentode	6-3	Heat	6.3	0.40	135	3.0	135	1.5	8200	370	1400	400	12000
69	Spec detector	6-2	Heat	6.3	0.30	135	3.5		1.5	64500	320	1450	900	11000
71-A	Power amp	4-1	Fil.	5.0	0.25	180	5.0		9.0	20700	9.0	1620	1600	10200
85	Diode-triode	6-4	Heat	6.3	0.30	180	14.0		13.5	1850	90.0	1570		
89	Three-Grid amp (B amplifier)	6-1	Heat	6.3	0.40	250	4.5	135	3.0	8300	30.0	1635		
	(As pentode)					160	20.0		43.0	3000	3.0	425		
99	Gen purpose	4-1	Fil	3.3	0.06	90	7.0		20.0	82500	8.3	1500		
182B	Power amp	4-1	Heat	5.0	1.25	200	17.0		20.0	15500	9.7	1800		
183	Power amp	4-1	Fil	5.0	1.25	250	3.0	180	18.0	3330	135	1330		
210	Power amp	4-1	Fil	7.5	1.25	250	20.0		4.5	1670	6.6	1550		
						350	2.5		29.0	6000	5.0	1600		
						125	18.0		60.0	5150	3.0			

Continued on page 160

CHARACTERISTICS OF THERMIONIC VACUUM TUBES

Type No	Purpose	Base	Cathode Type	Cathode Voltage	Cathode Current amp.	Plate voltage	Plate current mA	Screen voltage	Grid bias volts	Plate resist. ohms	Amp factor	Mutual cond. μ umho	Power output m watts	Load resist. ohms
257	Power pentode	5-4	Fil	5.0	0.30	110	20.0	110	21.5	41000	55.0	1350	800	6000
401	Gen purpose	4-1	Fil	5.0	1.00	90	3.0		4.5	10000	8.0	1000		
402	Power output	4-1	Fil	3.0	1.50	80	20.0		40.0	2000	3.0	1000		20000
291	A.F amp	5-1	Heat	12.3	0.30	120	3.0		11.0	8700	6.8	780		3000
293	A.F amp	5-1 (Output Stage)	Heat	6.3	0.60	120	30.0		11.0	400	11.2	2550	1250	100000
						173	4.0		6.5					8000
295	A.F amp	5-1 (Output Stage)	Heat	2.5	4	180	1.5		6.5				1250	500
						250	4.0		14.0				4500	300
483	Power output	4-1	Fil	5.0	1.35	250	52.0		40.5	12000	14.4	1200		
484	Gen purpose	4-1	Fil	3.0	1.30	180	15.3		3.0	3000	13.0	4350		
485	Gen purpose	5-1	Heat	3.0	1.30	135	6.0		6.0	2450	3.3	1340		
LA	Output tube		Fil	6.3	0.30	135	5.5	135	6.0	8900	12.5	1400	700	9500
KR-5	Output pentode		Fil	6.3	0.30	135	12.0	165	9.0	5260	12.5	1400	1200	8000
KR20	Two-grid det		Heat	2.5	1.00	165	17.0		11.0	47000	100	1900		100000
KR22	Two-grid det		Heat	6.3	0.40	250	3.5	250	0	10000	100	2100		100000
KR25	Output pentode		Heat	2.5	1.75	250	3.5	180	14.0	10000	14.0	1400	3000	9000
GA	Pentode		Fil	5.0	0.25	180	34.0	250	14.0	100000	14.0	1400	800	7000
18	Output pentode	6-3	Heat	14.0	0.30	250	7.5		20	30000	20	2200	3000	9000
75	Double diode High-mu triode	6-4	Heat	6.3	0.30	250	34.0		50.0	5000	50.0	2000		
						250	0.8		16.5	91000	165	2200		
8	Triple grid Amp anddet 3-Grid amp	6-4	Heat	6.3	0.3	250	2.3	100	3.0	1.5 meg	100	1100		
		6-4	Heat	6.3	0.3	250	0.1	100	6.0		1875	1250		
						180	4.0	5	3.0	1 meg	1875			
						250	10.5	125	3.0	600000	1100			
2A5	Output pentode	6-2	Heat	2.5	1.5	250	34.0	250	16.5	500	990	1650	3000	9000
2A7	Pentagrid	7-2	Heat	2.5	0.80	250	4.0	100	3.0	300000	165	2200		
6A7	Pentagrid	7-2	Heat	6.3	0.3	250	4.0	100	3.0	300000		475		
2B7	2-Diode pentode	7-2	Heat	2.5	0.80	250	6.0	100	3.0	800000	800	475		
6B7	2-Diode pentode	7-2	Heat	6.3	0.30	250	6.0	100	9.0	800000	800	1000		
864	Amp and det	4-1	Fil	1.1	0.25	135	2.9		4.5	13500	8.2	610		200000
						90					8.2			

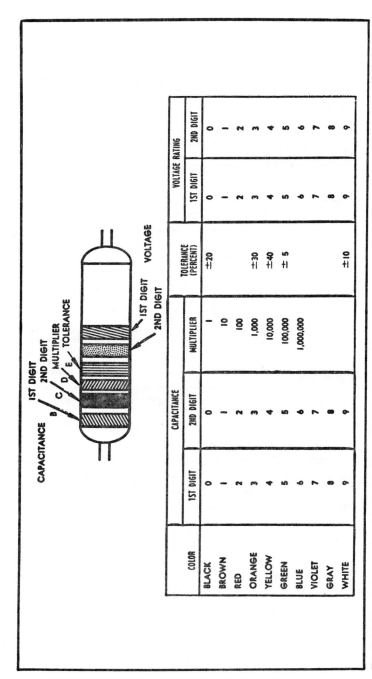

Fig. 8-10. The six-band color code for tubular paper-dielectric capacitors.

COLOR	CAPACITANCE			TOLERANCE (PERCENT)	VOLTAGE RATING	
	1ST DIGIT	2ND DIGIT	MULTIPLIER		1ST DIGIT	2ND DIGIT
BLACK	0	0	1	±20	0	0
BROWN	1	1	10		1	1
RED	2	2	100		2	2
ORANGE	3	3	1,000	±30	3	3
YELLOW	4	4	10,000	±40	4	4
GREEN	5	5	100,000	± 5	5	5
BLUE	6	6	1,000,000		6	6
VIOLET	7	7			7	7
GRAY	8	8			8	8
WHITE	9	9		±10	9	9

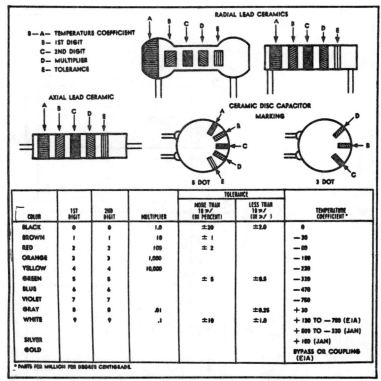

8—A— TEMPERATURE COEFFICIENT
B— 1ST DIGIT
C— 2ND DIGIT
D— MULTIPLIER
E— TOLERANCE

RADIAL LEAD CERAMICS

AXIAL LEAD CERAMIC

CERAMIC DISC CAPACITOR
MARKING

5 DOT

3 DOT

COLOR	1ST DIGIT	2ND DIGIT	MULTIPLIER	TOLERANCE MORE THAN 10 ꝑꝑ (IN PERCENT)	TOLERANCE LESS THAN 10 ꝑꝑ (IN ꝑꝑ)	TEMPERATURE COEFFICIENT*
BLACK	0	0	1.0	±20	±2.0	0
BROWN	1	1	10	± 1		—30
RED	2	2	100	± 2		—80
ORANGE	3	3	1,000			—150
YELLOW	4	4	10,000			—220
GREEN	5	5		± 5	±0.5	—330
BLUE	6	6				—470
VIOLET	7	7				—750
GRAY	8	8	.01		±0.25	+30
WHITE	9	9	.1	±10	±1.0	+120 TO —750 (EIA)
						+500 TO —330 (JAN)
SILVER						+100 (JAN)
GOLD						BYPASS OR COUPLING (EIA)

* PARTS PER MILLION PER DEGREE CENTIGRADE.

Fig. 8-11. Color code for ceramic capacitors having various configurations.

Fig. 8-1) is indicated by two figures, the first of which is the number of pins. These are mainly tubes used in the oldest radios (before 1935), and many of them are obsolete. For a more complete listing of tubes, including possible substitutes for the tubes in this table and tubes used in sets up to about 1950, refer to the date from the *RCA Receiving Tube Manual* in Appendix A.

Chapter 9
From the Author's Bag of Tricks

Keep 'em playing! That was the motto of radio fans back in World War II, when the diversion of industrial production from consumer goods to defense needs made new radios as scarce as hens' teeth. Those days were a real test of a radio repairman's ingenuity. To keep the old sets playing, we dreamed up many improvisations and expedients. What follows is a few ideas that will help the radio restorer of today to keep the sets of yesterday playing. These are just a few of the many ideas that can be used, but they should solve lots of problems and stimulate you to come up with some ideas of your own.

It is always best to replace defective parts in any radio set with identical parts. However, it is not always possible to do this. To handle such a situation, a good repairman makes emergency repairs or finds some way to make a substitution. These emergency repairs are not infallible. In circuits in which electrical characteristics are critical, these repairs may not work. For the most part, however, they will work under the conditions indicated.

Burned-out primaries and open secondaries of transformers can be repaired by using an rf choke or a resistor in place of the open winding and by connecting a coupling capacitor from primary to secondary. (See Fig. 9-1) A resistor for the primary may be from 50,000 to 150,000 ohms; for the secondary, from 0.5 to 2 megohms. The capacitor may be from 0.000025 μF to 0.0005 μF for radio frequency and from 0.01 to 0.1 μF for audio frequency. (See Fig.

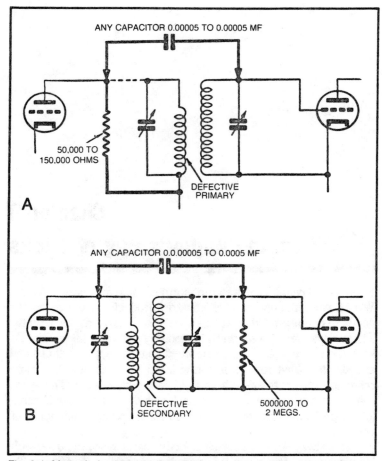

Fig. 9-1. Method of substituting a resistor and capacitor for open winding.

9-1). When one-half of a center-tapped secondary of an audio transformer burns out, substitution can be made as illustrated in Fig. 9-2.

Where a capacitor is not obtainable, a few turns of wire wound around the good winding or high rf lead and then connected to grid or plate, depending on which winding is open (Fig. 9-3), may give the desired coupling.

When a defect has been isolated to a particular stage in the set and a repair or replacement is not possible, the stage may be bridged by connecting a capacitor from the plate of the stage preceding the defective stage to the grid of the stage following the defective stage, as shown in Fig. 9-4. This will not work for detector stages. Use a

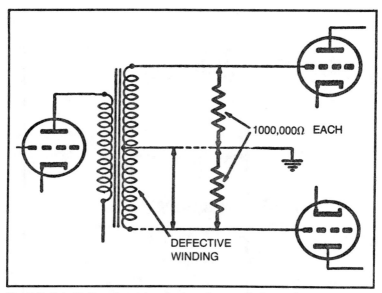

Fig. 9-2. Substitution of resistors for transformer winding.

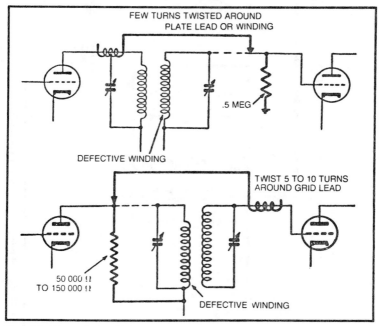

Fig. 9-3. Method of substituting a resistor and a few turns of wire for open winding.

165

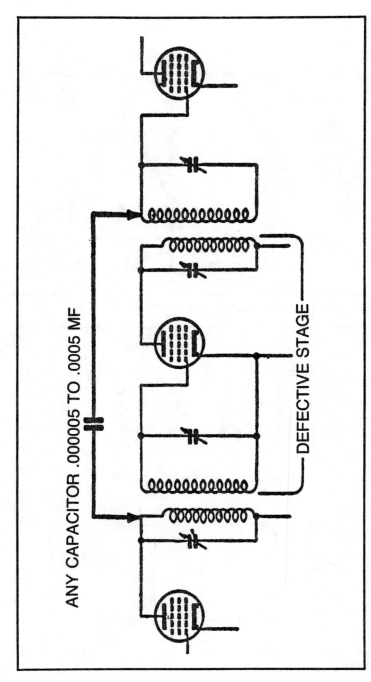

ANY CAPACITOR .000005 TO .0005 MF

DEFECTIVE STAGE

Fig. 9-4. Method of bridging defective stage.

166

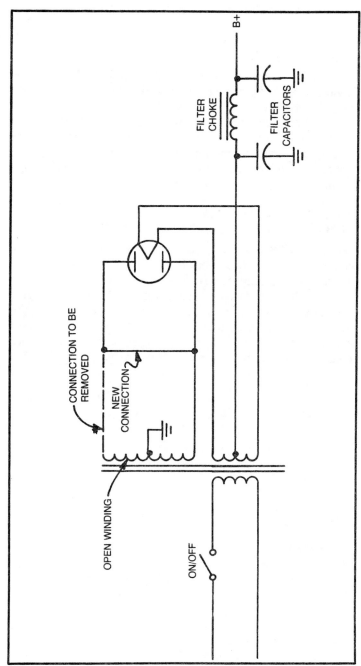

Fig. 9-5. Using a power transformer that has half of its high-voltage winding open.

167

0.0005-μF capacitor for rf and i-f stages; use a 0.01-μF capacitor for af stages.

CAPACITOR AS TEST INSTRUMENT

An ordinary bypass capacitor can be used to localize noise or oscillation (squeals). By connecting the capacitor between the grid and ground at the input of each stage, starting at the final stage, the trouble can be localized to the stage where the noise or oscillation is not affected by the capacitor. Shunting cathode, screen and plate bypass capacitors with a capacitor known to be good often shows open or partially open capacitors much quicker than disconnecting and testing each capacitor separately.

USING A POWER TRANSFORMER
WITH HALF OF THE HIGH-VOLTAGE WINDING OPEN

Sometimes it is possible to still use a power transformer even though there is an open in one-half of the secondary winding. If the transformer is in a full-wave rectifier circuit, the circuit can be converted to a half-wave circuit as shown in Fig. 9-5, thus bypassing the defective part of the winding. To do this, just remove the connection shown as a dashed line in Fig. 9-5 and add the new connection shown. This is a very easy change to make—much easier than installing a new transformer, even if you're lucky enough to find one.

Chapter 10
Receiver Tune Up
for Top Performance

This chapter shows how to adjust a radio to get all the performance that was designed into it. The tune-up procedure for a receiver is known as *alignment*. Not all restorers of antique radios will wish to try this procedure, especially when they are first getting into restoration, because it can be tricky and does require additional test equipment beyond the basic VOM or multimeter. Furthermore, it is at the very bottom of the list of things to do in restoring a receiver. For these reasons it is presented last in this book. However, alignment is a very useful procedure to know about. Alignment is often necessary to get top performance out of a radio and is occasionally necessary to get even acceptable performance.

BASIC CONCEPTS OF ALIGNMENT

The tuned circuits of a radio receiver must be accurately adjusted to work together if the set is to achieve its maximum degree of operational efficiency. When the circuits are thus correctly related to one another, they are said to be in *alignment*.

The fixed frequency difference between the rf signal carrier and the heterodyne oscillator must be maintained with a high degree of accuracy over the entire tuning range of the receiver. Simultaneous tuning of the rf and oscillator circuits is achieved by ganging the tuning capacitors (Fig. 10-1) and/or inductors (Fig. 10-2) of the separate circuits and making them responsive to a single control.

Fig. 10-1. Ganged tuning capacitor, showing trimmers that are adjusted during alignment.

The several capacitors or inductors are said to *track* if they retain their proper frequency relationships throughout the tuning range.

The aging of parts, the changing of the characteristics of tubes, climatic conditions and vibration are some of the reasons for misalignment. Also, haphazard attempts at alignment and tinkering often do more harm than good, and may increase the time spent on relatively minor repairs.

Every receiver that is operating poorly requires maintenance, but it does not follow that every receiver that needs maintenance needs alignment. Repairs which require replacement of components or the redressing of wiring especially in high-frequency circuits, often make subsequent alignment necessary.

The usual indication of the need for alignment is low sensitivity and volume even though everything else is *definitely* good. Alignment is also needed if the rf circuits do not track properly; that is, if the dial reading does not agree with the frequency of the incoming signal.

In some difficult troubleshooting problems, it may be necessary to attempt alignment to locate the trouble; for example, a shorted trimmer capacitor across a low-resistance coil. Resistance readings are difficult to interpret in a circuit such as this, but failure of the circuit to respond to peaking during alignment will show that there is something definitely wrong with the tuned circuit.

Another reason for alignment is the replacement of one or more tubes in critical circuits, such as oscillators. This illustrates the point that when slightly weak tubes are replaced with new ones, the circuit characteristics can change because of the different interelectrode capacities of the original and new tubes. This can detune the grid circuits and cause low sensitivity.

ALIGNMENT PRECAUTIONS

Before alignment is attempted, you should read carefully and follow all available service literature on the radio. There have been many instances where a receiver has been thrown out of alignment by tampering.

No adjustments of any kind should be made before it has been definitely established that component part troubles are not causing the abnormal operation. Attempting alignment when other troubles

Fig. 10-2. The ganged tuning inductors of a Sears Silvertone battery-operated model.

171

are present can lead to complete realignment after finding the other fault. Alignment is at the very bottom of the list of operations performed after troubleshooting.

The alignment procedures and adjustments recommended in this chapter are not meant to be used for all receivers; they are general. Use them only as a guide. The specific information on any receiver is contained in the service instructions written for that receiver. If the particular manual is not available, the general procedure in this chapter may be used.

- **Signal Generator.** An accurately calibrated rf signal generator is a prime necessity both for checking the alignment of a set and for aligning the circuits.

It is possible to do a rough job of alignment without a signal generator. Thus, trimmers and padders can be tuned for maximum output from the receiver, but the results obtained from this method are likely to be accurate.

- **Output Indicators.** For best results, an output indicator should be used. This can be the AC scale of a multimeter or VTVM.

The loudspeaker of a receiving set can be used as an output indicator as a last resort. With such a device, however, the results obtained will depend on the accuracy of the restorer's ear, and the human ear is not very sensitive to small changes in the level of sound. If a loudspeaker must be used, its output should be lowered as far as possible, and the weakest possible input signal should also be used. The signal should be weak in order to minimize or eliminate automatic gain control action, and the output should be lowered because the ear is best able to detect changes of sound level in the low-level range.

AM RECEIVER ALIGNMENT

In general, circuit alignment is best begun in the circuits that are farthest from the antenna. Adjustment then proceeds toward the antenna, with the antenna circuit proper usually being the last one adjusted.

In some receivers, it is necessary to disable the high-frequency oscillator so that unwanted beat frequencies cannot cause misleading signals. The oscillator tube can be removed from its socket, or the tuning capacitor can be shorted out to stop oscillations. This applies only to i-f alignment.

The AGC circuit may be used or may be cut out of service during the alignment of the set. If the AGC circuit uses a separate

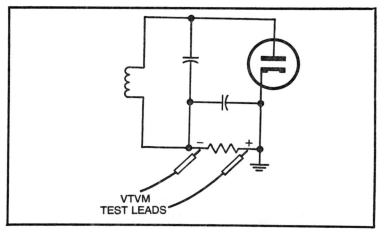

Fig. 10-3. Signal voltage measurement at the detector load.

tube, and it cannot be removed from its socket, the circuit can be disconnected at the common point to the stages that are AGC-controlled, or the AGC bus can be grounded.

Output Measurements

The signal output level at the detector is an effective measure of circuit alignment. This output can be measured by connecting an electronic multimeter across the detector load resistor (Fig. 10-3). An electronic multimeter is specified because a meter with a high sensitivity is required.

If the level at the detector is not strong enough to give a good reading on DC scale of the multimeter, an output meter, or the multimeter connected as an output meter by using the AC scale, may be connected to the audio output circuit. The meter test leads are connected to the voice coil (Fig. 10-4).

The signal output may be at a low level at this point also, depending on the sensitivity of the receiver. In this case, the connection shown in Fig. 10-5 can be used at the highest point of signal voltage in the receiver. A DC blocking capacitor should be connected in the hot lead to protect the meter. If a regular output meter is available, the external capacitor need not be included because there is one connected internally.

LOCATION OF TRIMMERS

Most i-f stages have double-tuned transformers; that is, the primaries and secondaries are separately tuned. Either adjustable

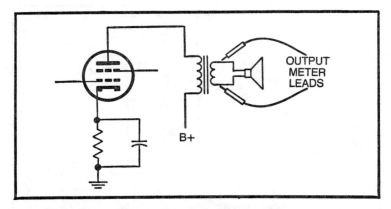

Fig. 10-4. Signal voltage measurement at the voice coil.

capacitors or tuning slugs may be used as trimmers. The i-f trimmers of old radios are usually small, adjustable mica capacitors that are located in a metal can along with the i-f transformer (see Fig. 10-6). Generally, both adjustment screws (primary and secondary) are located at the top or bottom of the i-f can. In some cases, one may be at the top and the other at the bottom of the can, both may be at the side of the can, or both may be on the chassis. In some cases, it is necessary to use a special nonmetallic screwdriver or hex wrench to adjust the screws since the inductive effect of a metallic screw driver or hex wrench might affect circuit tuning. Special alignment tools are available from any electronics distributor.

I-F ALIGNMENT

Before discussing alignment procedures, we assume that all alignment adjustments are not in their normal positions.

Alignment is begun at the final i-f stage. Set the signal generator to the desired frequency and turn on the modulation switch. Connect a blocking capacitor in the hot lead between the signal generator and the grid of the last i-f amplifier tube and ground. Connect the output meter or multimeter.

Turn the receiver gain controls on full, and set the signal generator attenuator to produce a midscale reading on the output meter. Adjust the primary and secondary trimmers in the output i-f amplifier for maximum output.

Move the signal generator connection to the grid of the next i-f tube toward the antenna, and adjust the trimmers of the stage for maximum output. The output of the signal generator must now be decreased because the signal strength has been increased by the additional amplification of this stage.

Other i-f stages, if any, are aligned in the same manner. It is very important not to change the frequency of the signal generator during the alignment.

Mixer Output Alignment

Because the frequency of the mixer output signal is the same as the i-f frequency, the same signal frequency that was fed into the i-f stages can be fed into the mixer. Feed the signal into the grid of the mixer. Adjust the trimmers in the i-f transformer between the mixer plate and the first i-f grid for maximum indication on the output meter.

In some receivers, it may be very difficult to get at the underside of the mixer tube socket, especially in vhf circuits. Connect the signal generator hot lead to a metal tube shield. Push the shield down over the tube, but not so far that it touches the chassis. The signal will reach the grid by capacitive coupling. If a suitable shield is not available, wrap the signal generator lead around the mixer tube.

All of the circuits that are tuned to the i-f frequency have now been aligned. At this point, the stages that were aligned previously can be touched up, with the signal generator connected to the mixer circuit. The purpose of this touching up or retuning procedure is to compensate for the slight change in frequency that often takes place because of interaction between stages during alignment.

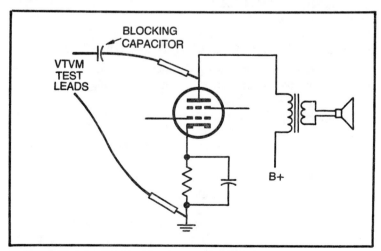

Fig. 10-5. Signal voltage measurement in the plate circuit.

175

OSCILLATOR, MIXER INPUT AND RF ALIGNMENT

Aligning the rf amplifier stages, local oscillator and the mixer grid circuit is similar to aligning the i-f circuits to track with the tuning dial. The rf trimmers are usually built into the main tuning capacitor (Fig. 10-1). The other trimmers and padders are often small, adjustable mica capacitors, as shown in Fig. 10-7. (A padder is a trimmer capacitor in the oscillator circuit that is used for calibration at the low-frequency end of the tuning dial).

Set the receiver tuning dial to the highest frequency on the dial (on multiband receivers, the highest frequency of the band being aligned). Connect the signal generator to the antenna input and tune it to the same frequency as the receiver. Connect an output indicator and adjust the trimmer of each circuit for a maximum output indication as above.

Check the accuracy of the tracking. Set the signal generator to a frequency near the middle of the tuning range of the band under alignment. Tune the receiver to this frequency. If the signal from the generator produces a maximum output indication when the receiver is tuned to exactly the same frequency as the generator, then the receiver dial is tracking properly. If these results are not obtained, however, you will need to repeat the whole procedure. (Sometimes the adjustment of the padders will affect the alignment of the high-frequency end of the dial.)

Some receivers have adjustable inductors or capacitors only on the oscillator circuit for the low end of the dial. In these cases, it is still necessary to check the tracking of the dial at one or more intermediate places.

ALIGNING RECEIVERS WITH MORE THAN ONE TUNING RANGE

Receivers with more than one tuning range are aligned in the same way as one-band receivers. Each band is aligned beginning with the highest frequency.

The signal generator and receiver are set to the frequencies that are designated in the instructions. After one band is aligned, the next one is aligned in the same way, but the frequencies involved are different.

If there is not information on the location of the adjusting screws, they can be found by experimentation. Tune the receiver to a high frequency and set the signal generator to the same frequency. Note the band in use at the time. Turn the trimmers or other adjustment screws—one at a time—until the one that affects the output is found. Return all adjusting screws as closely as possible to

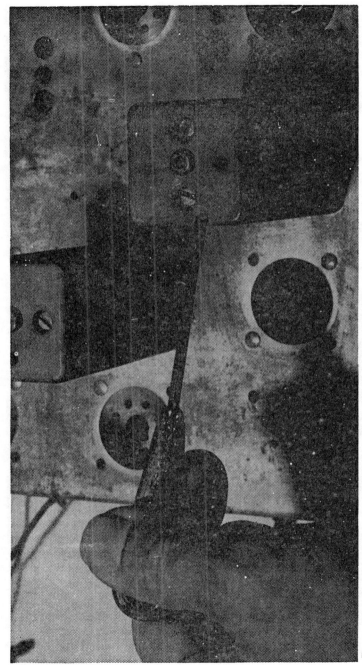

Fig. 10-6. Intermediate-frequency trimmers typical of those found in old radios.

Fig. 10-7. Some trimmers take the form of small variable mica capacitors such as this one.

their original positions. The fact that one affects the output means that the adjustment is in the circuit of the band in use. In some higher frequency units, the mere touching of a trimmer with an alignment tool can cause a change in the output. Because a given change in capacitance will be noticed more readily at higher frequencies, it is best to make the test at the high-frequency end of each band.

Fig. 10-8. A view of the chassis of the Silvertone Model 7108, showing the unusual ganged tuning inductor and foil-lined cardboard tube shield.

Fig. 10-9. This Zenith Wavemagnet looks as though it would really "pull in the stations."

Trimmers in a multiband receiver are usually located in groups near the coils they tune. The trimmer associated with the band in use can be identified by the relative number of turns on the coil. Because the coil for the lowest frequency band will have the greatest number of turns, the coil in use can be identified by the number of its turns as compared with the turns on the other coils.

One of the wonderful things about antique radios is the diversity of them. It's surprising the things you find in them. The *Silvertone* (Sears, Roebuck and Company) Model 7108, for example, had a three-stage ganged tuning inductor (Fig. 10-8) instead of the usual tuning capacitor. Unusual circuit features such as this can complicate alignment procedures. Servicing information provided by the manufacturer or a publisher such as Gernsback, Rider, or Supreme is very helpful in such cases. This radio, by the way, had a No. 625 camera battery (small button type) in the circuit, though not in the schematic. Apparently it was added by a serviceman for some reason that now escapes me. This set also had cardboard tube shields (Fig. 10-8). The inner surface of the shield was metal foil, which contacted the tube base when the shield was pushed down over the tube.

The *Zenith* Model 6G601M was an early portable. Like portables made by Zenith for quite a number of years, it had a detachable loop antenna called a *Wavemagnet*. Apparently the manufacturer didn't want to leave too much to the radio buyer's imagination at this point, because the antenna actually had a giant horseshoe magnet printed on it (Fig. 10-9). This antenna didn't have any special capability for pulling in stations—it was really just a loop antenna—but the printed magnet did suggest the way to point the antenna for best reception. Loop antennas in later Zenith models were without the printed magnet, but they were still called *Wavemagnets*.

Chapter 11
Advanced Radio Theory

This information is not required in order to use the testing, adjustments and other service procedures in this book. It is presented for those readers desiring more information about how a radio works, simply as a matter of interest or because they wish to do servicing of an advanced nature.

TUBE FUNCTIONS

The functions performed by electron tubes are many and varied, but for convenience these functions may be consolidated into a few general groups. Each function is determined not only by the tube type but also by the circuit and its associated apparatus.

A general capability of the electron tube is to alter an AC (alternating current) so that it becomes a pulsating DC (direct current), as shown in Fig. 11-1.

Associated apparatus can smooth out the variations in the current, and the system as a whole can be said to change an alternating current into a constant-amplitude direct current. This function provides convenient sources of DC voltage when the only available primary source of electrical energy is an AC power line or an AC generator. These DC voltages may be as low as a fraction of a volt and as high as tens of thousands of volts. The action of changing an alternating current into a pulsating direct current is referred to in general terms as *rectification*. The electron tube which does this is called a *rectifier*.

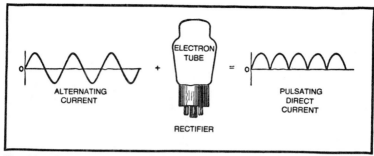

Fig. 11-1. Function of tube as rectifier of alternating current.

Another significant and useful capability of the electron tube, and perhaps its most important function, is described as *amplification* (Fig. 11-2). A stronger signal voltage may be obtained from the tube than is fed into it. In effect, the tube is a signal voltage magnifier. A signal equal to 1 volt fed into the input system of the amplifying tube may appear as 20 volts at its output. Different arrangements provide for different amounts of signal amplification.

This amplification ability accounts for the advanced development of modern-day communication. It is the basis of all long-distance telephony, because microwave amplifiers compensate for the energy losses encountered in transmission. Also public address systems amplify the voice of an individual so that thousands of people gathered together may hear it clearly.

Amplification makes radar possible because it strengthens the echo signal received from the target so that it can be made visible on a special screen. It is responsible for Teletype® operation. Television would be impossible without it. Amplification is essential in radio transmitters and receivers of all kinds to increase electrical energy

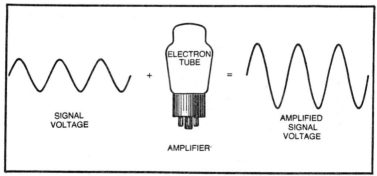

Fig. 11-2. Function of tube as amplifier.

183

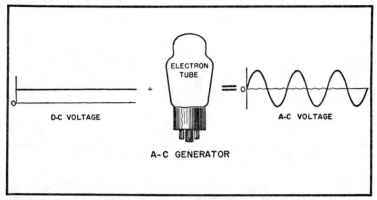

Fig. 11-3. Function of electron tube as generator of alternating current.

to proportions necessary for proper operation of the various circuits of the equipment.

Still another extremely important facility offered by the vacuum tube is the conversion of electrical energy existing as direct current and voltage into alternating current and voltage (Fig. 11-3). Used in this manner, the tube draws energy from a DC source and, in conjunction with suitable apparatus, *generates* high-frequency oscillations. This function has been responsible for innumerable developments in the communication field.

The principle of oscillation underlies the operation of virtually every type of radio transmitter, large or small, fixed or portable. As a generator of high-frequency oscillation, the electron tube replaced ponderous rotating machinery. Even more important is that specialized oscillators opened up the very-high- and ultra-high-frequency and microwave regions for operation. These extend from approximately 30 MHz to tens of thousands of megahertz. The use of these frequencies has helped to overcome the communication limitations caused by changing seasons and the effects of weather. It helped create new techniques, among which are radar, television and microwave cooking.

Availability of these high-frequencies for communications has made possible the convenient use of low power and the design of small receivers, transmitters and antennas.

The electron tube can modify the shape of electric current and voltage waveforms; that is, it can change the amplitude of these quantities relative to time. Voltage and current shaping (Figs. 11-4 and 11-5) are vital to the operation of numerous electronic devices. It is used in code transmission, the timing of circuit actions in radar,

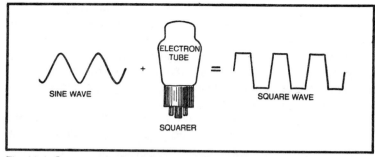

Fig. 11-4. One type of waveshaping accomplished by electron tubes. The input signal is a sine wave; the output is a square wave.

in the production of television pictures and in the operation of Teletype® equipment. Electronic computers could not operate without waveshaping of the currents and voltages present in the equipment.

ELECTRON-TUBE RADIO RECEIVERS

At the radio transmitter, the carrier frequency is modulated by the desired signal, which may consist of coded characters, voice, music, or other types of signals. Amplitude modulation (AM) occurs if the signals cause the amplitude of the output to vary. Frequency modulation (FM) occurs if the signals cause the frequency of the carrier, or center frequency, to vary. Although there are other types of modulation, only AM receivers will be treated in this chapter.

The rf carrier wave with the modulating signal impressed upon it is transmitted through space as an electromagnetic wave to the antenna of the receiver. As the wave passes across the receiving antenna, small AC voltages are induced in the antenna. These

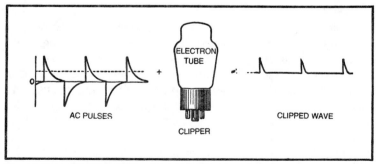

Fig. 11-5. Another type of waveshaping. Only parts of the positive peaks of the input signal are present in the output.

voltages are coupled into the receiver via the antenna coupling coil. The function of the receiver is to select the desired carrier frequency from those present in the antenna circuit and to amplify the small AC signal voltage. The receiver then removes the carrier by the process of detection (rectification and the removal of the rf component) and amplifies the resultant audio signal to the proper magnitude to operate the loudspeaker or earphones.

Two major types of radio receivers are covered here—the tuned-radio-frequency (trf) receiver, and the superheterodyne receiver.

TRF RECEIVERS

The tuned-radio-frequency receiver, generally known as the trf receiver, consists of one or more rf stages, a detector stage, one or more af stages, a reproducer and the necessary power supply. A block diagram of a trf receiver is shown in Fig. 11-6. The waveforms that appear in the respective sections of the receiver are shown below the block diagram.

The amplitude of the AM signal at the input of the receiver is relatively small because it has been attenuated in the space between the transmitter and the receiver. It is composed of the carrier frequency and the modulation envelope. The rf amplifier stages amplify the waveform, but they do not change its basic shape if the circuits are operating properly. The detector rectifies and removes the rf component of the signal. The output of the detector is a weak signal made up only of the modulation component, or envelope, of the incoming signal. The af amplifier stages following the detector increase the amplitude of the af signal to a value sufficient to operate the loudspeaker or earphones.

RF Section

The antenna-ground system serves to introduce the desired signal into the first rf amplifier stage via the antenna coupling transformer. For best reception, the resistance of the antenna-ground system should be low. The antenna should also be of the proper length for the band of frequencies to be received, and the antenna impedance should match the input impedance of the receiver. The gain of most commercial receivers, however, is generally sufficient to make these values noncritical.

The rf amplifiers in the trf receiver have tunable tanks in the grid circuits. Thus, the receiver may be tuned so that only one rf signal within its tuning range is selected for amplification. When the

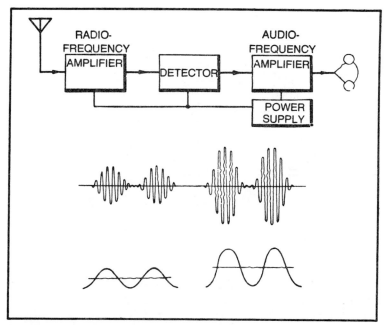

Fig. 11-6. Block diagram of a trf receiver and waveforms.

tank is tuned to the desired frequency, it resonates and produces a relatively large circulating current. The grid of the rf amplifier then receives a relatively large signal voltage at the resonant frequency, and minimum signals at other frequencies.

The relative ability of a receiver to select one particular frequency and to reject all others is called the *selectivity* of the receiver. The relative ability of the receiver to amplify small signal voltages is called the *sensitivity* of the receiver. Both of these values may be improved by increasing the number of rf stages. When this is done, the tuning capacitors in the grid tank circuits are usually ganged on the same shaft, and trimmers are added in parallel with each capacitor to make the stages track at the same frequency. In addition, the outer plates of the rotor sections of the capacitors are sometimes slotted to enable more precise alignment throughout the tuning range.

Tetrodes or pentodes are generally used in rf amplifiers because, unlike triodes, they do not usually require neutralization. They also have higher gain than triodes.

A typical rf amplifier stage employing a pentode is shown in Fig. 11-7. Tuned circuit L_2C_1 is inductively coupled to L_1, the antenna

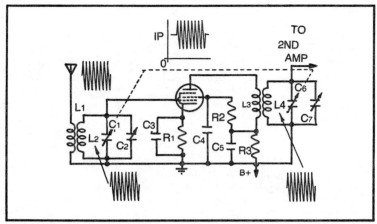

Fig. 11-7. An rf amplifier stage.

coil. R_1 and C_3 provide operating bias for the tube. C_4 and R_2 are the screen bypass capacitor and dropping resistor, respectively. The tuned circuit, L_4C_6, couples the following stage inductively to L_3. Both transformers are of the air-core type. The dotted lines indicate mechanical ganging of C_1 and C_6 on the same shaft. The tuning capacitor in the next stage is also ganged on the same shaft.

If you want the receiver to cover more than one frequency range, use additional coils that have the proper inductance. They are sometimes of the plug-in variety, but more generally they are mounted on the receiver and their leads are connected to a multicontact rotary switch. The latter method is preferable for band switching because the desired band can be selected simply by turning the switch. The same tuning capacitor is used for each band. However, when band switching is employed, the trimmers are connected across the individual tuning inductors and not across the main tuning capacitors.

Decoupling circuits are designed for both rf and af amplifiers to counteract feedback. Thus, in the rf amplifier in Fig. 11-7, C_5 and R_3 make up the decoupling circuit. R_3 offers a high impedance to the signal current, but C_5 offers a low impedance. Consequently, the signal current is shunted to ground around the B+ supply. Because R_3 also offers a high resistance to DC current, it may be replaced by a choke coil having a high impedance only to the signal current. Each stage is similarly equipped with a decoupling circuit.

A mechanical or an electrical bandspread may be used as an aid in separating stations that are crowded together on the tuning dial.

188

Mechanical bandspread is simply a micrometer arrangement to reduce the motion of the capacitor rotor as the tuning knob is turned. When electrical bandspread is used, a small variable capacitor is connected in parallel with the tuning capacitor. Because of its small size, you can move this variable capacitor a considerable amount before it causes an appreciable change in the frequency of the tuned circuit. If the tuning capacitors are ganged, the bandspread capacitors are also ganged.

Detector

The process of removing the intelligence component of the modulated waveform from the rf carrier is called detection or demodulation. In the AM system, the audio or intelligence component causes both the positive and the negative half cycles of the rf wave to vary in amplitude. The function of the detector is to rectify the modulated signal. A suitable filter eliminates the remaining rf pulses and passes the audio component on the af amplifiers.

Details of the various methods of detection will be discussed in a subsequent paragraph. Each of the several methods that might be used in the trf receiver have certain inherent weaknesses. For example, the diode detector requires several stages of amplification ahead of the detector. It loads its tuned input circuit, and therefore, the sensitivity and selectivity of the circuit are reduced. However, it can handle strong signals without overloading, and its linearity is good.

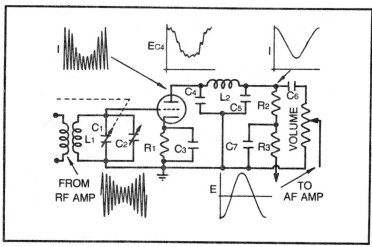

Fig. 11-8. Plate detector circuit.

The grid-leak detector is sensitive—and consequently requires fewer stages of amplification—but it has poor linearity and selectively. Also, it can be overloaded on strong signals.

The circuit shown in Fig. 11-8 employs plate detection. It has medium sensitivity and the ability to handle strong signals without overloading. The selectivity of this circuit is excellent, but because the i_p: e_g (plate current verses grid voltage) graph is curved near the cutoff point (where the plate detector operates), some distortion in the output cannot be avoided.

In Fig. 11-8, the tube is biased nearly to cutoff by the average plate current that flows through R_1. This average value increases as the signal strength increases. On positive half cycles of the incoming signals the plate current varies with the amplitude of the modulating wave and produces the desired af output voltage. On negative half cycles no appreciable plate current flows. Between positive half cycles the bias voltage is held constant across R_1 by the action of C_3, because the time constant of R_1C_3 is long compared with the time for the lowest af cycle.

The rf pulses are filtered out by means of a low-pass filter (consisting of C_4, L_2 and C_5), which rejects the rf component and passes the af compnonet. C_6 couples the af component to the first audio amplifier. R_2 is the plate load resistor, and the combination R_3C_7 makes up the decoupling circuit.

AF Section

The function of the af section of a receiver is to further amplify the audio signal, which is commonly fed via the volume control to the grid of the first audio amplifier tube. In most cases, the amount of amplification that is necessary depends on the type of reproducer used. If the reproducer consists of earphones, only one stage amplification might be necessary. If the reproducer is a large speaker or other mechanical device requiring a large amount of power, you might need several stages. In most receivers, the last af stage is operated as a power amplifier.

A necessary part of the af section is some means of manual control of the output signal level of the receiver. A manual volume control may be employed in a number of receiver circuits. Normally this control varies the amplitude of the signal applied to the grid of an amplifier tube, as shown in Fig. 11-8. Increasing the resistance between ground and the sliding contact increases the amplitude of the signal applied to the grid of the driven stage.

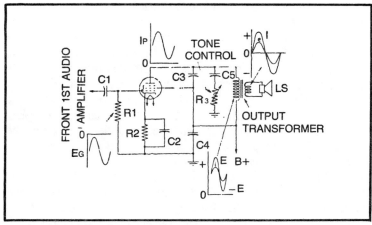

Fig. 11-9. Audio amplifier output stage.

An af output stage is shown in Fig. 11-9. C1 couples the first af amplifier to the output stage, and R1 is the grid coupling resistor. R2 and C2 provide a steady bias. Because of the low frequencies involved, C2 should have a larger value of capacitance than similar bypass capacitors in the rf section. C4 is the plate-bypass capacitor, or decoupling capacitor. C3 has a small value of capacitance and bypasses some of the higher frequencies around the output transformer, thus emphasizing the bass. The impedance of the primary of the output transformer commonly represents a compromise between maximum power transfer and minimum distortion. The impedance of the secondary is chosen to match the impedance of the voice coil. Some secondaries have taps on the windings to permit an impedance match to a variety of voice-coil impedances.

Tone control is usable. The purpose of tone control is to emphasize either low or high frequencies by shunting the undesired frequencies around the remainder of the circuit components in the audio section. A simple tone-control circuit, such as the series capacitor C5 and variable resistor R3 combination shown in Fig. 11-9, can be connected between plate and ground or between grid and ground in any of the audio stages of a receiver. In this figure, it is connected between plate and ground. The value of the series capacitor is such that it will bypass to ground the high-frequency components. The amount of high-frequency energy removed by the tone-control circuit is determined by the setting of the variable-resistor control arm. When the resistance is low, the high frequencies are attenuated; when it is high, they appear in the output.

Feedback voltage from output to input is sometimes developed across the impedance of the common power supply. For frequencies within the usable audio range, this impedance is sufficiently low so that insufficient feedback is obtained to cause oscillation. However, for extremely low frequencies, the capacitors in the power supply will sometimes have enough impedance to cause oscillation.

When two or more audio amplifier stages are supplied from a common B+ supply, feedback occurs as a result of common coupling between the plate circuits, and some method of decoupling must be employed. The coupling consists of the internal impedance of the source of plate voltage. The feedback may either increase or decrease the amplification, depending on the phase relation between the input voltage and the feedback voltage. In a multistage amplifier, the greatest transfer of feedback energy occurs between the final and first stages because of the high amplification through the multi-stage amplifier.

The effects of feedback are important if the feedback voltage coupled into the plate circuit of the first stage is appreciable compared to the signal voltage that would be developed if feedback did not exist. For example, a three-stage resistance-coupled amplifier may develop a feedback voltage (coupled via the B+ supply into the plate circuit of stage 1) which is in phase with the signal voltage of stage 1 and hence may cause oscillations to be set up. In audio amplifiers having high gain and a good low-frequency response, this regeneration causes the low-frequency oscillation known as "motor-boating."

Design engineers usually decouple plate circuits by adding a series resistor to the input stage, between its plate load and B+, and bypassing that resistor to ground. The appearance of motorboating means you need to replace either the decoupling resistor or its bypass capacitor.

Circuit of the trf Receiver

The complete circuit of a trf radio receiver operated from an AC power supply is shown in Fig. 11-10. The receiver uses two pentodes in the rf section, one triode operated as a plate detector and two pentode af amplifier stages to feed the loudspeaker.

From previous discussions, the various circuits may be identified and the signal may be traced from the antenna-ground system to the loudspeaker. The dotted lines indicate that the three main tuning capacitors are ganged on a single shaft. Across each of the main tuning capacitors is connected a trimmer capacitor to enable circuit

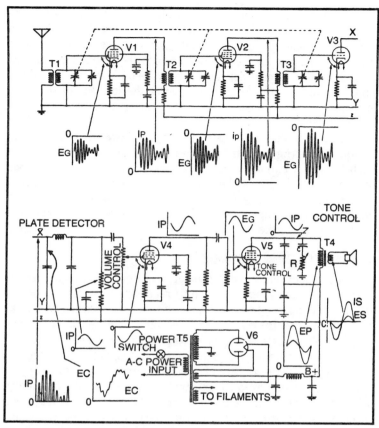

Fig. 11-10. Circuit of a complete trf receiver.

alignment. The ground circuit and the various decoupling circuits may be readily identified. The power supply voltage is obtained from a conventional full-wave rectifier. Rectifier and tube filament currents are obtained from two low-voltage windings on the power transformer.

Characteristics of the trf Receiver

The principal disadvantage of the trf receiver is that its selectivity, or its ability to separate signals, does not remain constant over its tuning range. As the set is tuned from the low-frequency end of its tuning range to the high-frequency end, its selectivity decreases.

Also, the amplification, or gain, of a trf receiver is not constant over the tuning range of the receiver. The gain depends on rf transformer gain, which increases with frequency. In order to improve the gain at the low-frequency end of the band, rf transformers employing high-impedance (untuned) primaries are designed so that the primary inductance will resonate with the primary distributed capacitance at some frequency slightly below the low end of the tunable band. Thus, the gain is good at the low end of the band because of the resonant buildup of primary current. The near-resonant condition of the primary at the low end more than offsets the effect of reduced transformer action. However, the shunting action of the primary distributed capacitance lowers the gain at the high-frequency end of the band. To make up for the resultant poor gain at the high end of the band, a small capacitor is connected between the plate and grid leads of adjacent rf stages to supplement the transformer coupling. At the low end of the band, the capacitive coupling is negligible.

SUPERHETERODYNE RECEIVERS

The superheterodyne receiver was developed to overcome many of the disadvantages of the trf receiver. The essential difference between the trf receiver and the superheterodyne receiver is that in the former the rf amplifiers preceding the detector are tunable over a band of frequencies, whereas in the latter the corresponding amplifiers are tuned to one fixed frequency called the intermediate frequency (i-f). The principle of frequency conversion by heterodyne action is here employed to convert any desired station frequency within the receiver range to this intermediate frequency. Thus, an incoming signal is converted to the fixed intermediate frequency before detecting the audio signal component, and the i-f amplifier operates under uniformly optimum conditions throughout the receiver range. The i-f circuits can then have uniform selectivity, uniformly high voltage gain and uniform, satisfactory bandwidth to contain all of the desired sideband components associated with the amplitude modulated carrier.

The block diagram of a typical superheterodyne receiver is shown in Fig. 11-11. Below corresponding sections of the receiver are shown the waveforms of the signal at that point. The rf signal from the antenna passes first through an rf amplifier (preselector) where the amplitude of the signal is increased. A locally generated unmodulated rf signal of constant amplitude is then mixed with the carrier frequency in the mixer stage. The mixing, or heterodyning, of these two frequencies produces an intermediate frequency signal which contains all of the modulation characteristics of the original

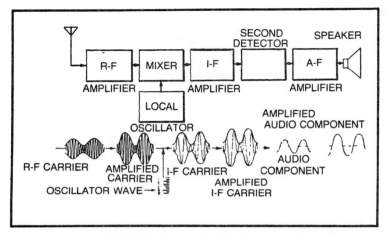

Fig. 11-11. Block diagram of a superheterodyne receiver and waveforms.

signal. The intermediate frequency is equal to the difference between the station frequency and the oscillator frequency associated with the heterodyne mixer. The intermediate frequency is then amplified in one or more stages called intermediate-frequency (i-f) amplifiers and fed to a conventional detector for recovery of the audio signal.

The detected signal is amplified in the af section and then fed to a headset or loudspeaker. The detector, the af section and the reproducer of a superheterodyne receiver are basically the same as those in a trf set, except that diode detection is generally used in the superheterodyne receiver. Automatic volume control or automatic gain control also is commonly employed in the superheterodyne receiver.

RF Amplifier

If an rf amplifier is used ahead of the mixer stage of a superheterodyne receiver, it is generally of conventional design. Besides amplifying the rf signal, the rf amplifier has other important functions. For example, it isolates the local oscillator from the antenna ground system. If the antenna were connected directly to the mixer stage, a part of the local oscillator signal might be radiated into space and cause interference. For this reason and others, superheterodyne receivers are provided with at least one rf amplifier stage.

Also, if the mixer stage were connected directly to the antenna, unwanted signals, called *images*, might be received, because the

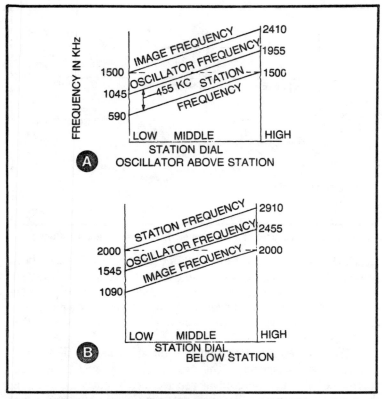

Fig. 11-12. Relation of image frequency to station frequency in a superheterodyne receiver.

mixer stage produces the intermediate frequency by heterodyning two signals whose frequency difference equals the intermediate frequency. (The heterodyne principle is treated later in this chapter.)

The image frequency always differs from the desired station frequency by twice the intermediate frequency. Image frequency is the station frequency plus or minus two times intermediate frequency. The image frequency is higher than the station frequency if the local oscillator frequency tracks (operates) above the station frequency (Fig. 11-12A). The image frequency is lower than the station frequency if the local oscillator tracks below the station frequency (Fig. 11-12B). The latter arrangement is generally used for the higher frequency bands, and the former for the lower frequency bands.

196

For example, if such a receiver having an intermediate frequency of 455 kHz is tuned to receive a station frequency of 1500 kHz (Fig. 11-12A), and the local oscillator has a frequency of 1955 kHz, the output of the i-f amplifier may contain two interfering signals—one from the 1500 kHz station and the other from an image station of 2410 kHz (1500 + 2 × 455 = 2410 kHz). The same receiver tuned near the low end of the band to a 590 kHz station has a local oscillator frequency of 1045 kHz. The output of the i-f amplifier contains the station signal (1045 − 590 = 455 kHz) and an image signal (1500 − 1045 = 455 kHz). Thus, the 1500 kHz signal is an image heard simultaneously with the 590 kHz station signal.

It may also be possible for any two signals having sufficient strength, and separated by the intermediate frequency to produce unwanted signals in the reproducer. The selectivity of the preselector tends to reduce the strength of these images and unwanted signals.

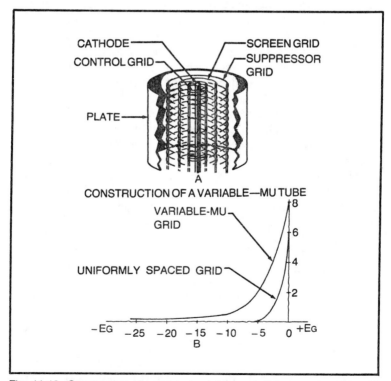

Fig. 11-13. Construction of variable-mu tubes and plate-current-versus-grid voltage curves.

The ratio of the amplitude of the desired station signal to that of the image is called the image rejection ratio and is an important characteristic of a superheterodyne receiver. Better super-heterodyne receivers are therefore equipped with one or more preselector stages, a typical example of which is shown in Fig. 11-14.

The amplification of a tube may be controlled by varying the bias voltage applied to the grid, but normally the range of this control is limited by the cutoff bias and the permissible distortion. In receivers employing automatic volume control (AVC) in the rf amplifier section, the amplification is varied over a wide range so that strong or weak signals may be accommodated. To permit this increased range of volume control, the variable-mu tube was developed. This tube is also known as the supercontrol or remote cutoff type.

The only difference in construction between variable-mu tubes and normal, or sharp cutoff, tubes is in the spacing between the turns of the control grid. In sharp cutoff tubes the turns of the grid wires are equally spaced, while in remote cutoff types the grid turns are closely spaced at the ends and widely spaced in the center. The construction of variable-mu tubes is shown in Fig. 11-13A.

With a small bias voltage, electrons flow through all the spaces of the grid and the amplification factor is relatively large because of the close spacing of the end turns of the control grid. As the bias is increased, the electron flow is cut off through the narrow spaces at the ends of the grid structure. However, they are still able to pass through the relatively large spaces at the center of the grid. The increased bias causes a decrease in the amplification due to the coarser turns in the central portion of the grid. A much greater value of bias is required to cut off the plate current flow in this type of tube. The remote-cutoff tube is so named because the cutoff bias value is greater than (more remote from) the value required to cut off plate current flow in tubes of evenly spaced turns.

Figure 11-13B shows the i_p:e_g (plate versus grid voltage) curves for both a conventional sharp cutoff tube and a variable-mu or remote-cutoff tube. The cutoff bias for the normal tube is -5 volts, and because the slope is almost constant, any change in bias produces little change in amplification. Contrasted with this characteristic, the curve for the variable-mu tube has a pronounced change in slope as the grid bias is increased from -10 volts to -15 volts and a small value of plate current is still flowing at a bias of -25 volts. The changing slope of this curve indicates a variation of amplification with bias. Thus, if a variable-mu tube is used with a bias source that varies with the signal strength, (AVC bus in Fig. 11-14), the output signal can be made substantially independent of the input signal strength.

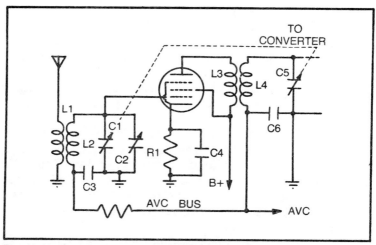

Fig. 11-14. Typical superheterodyne preselector stage.

The preselector stage shown in Fig. 11-14 employs a variable-mu tube and cathode bias. L_1 is the antenna coil, L2 and C1 make up the tuned input circuit and C2 is the trimmer used for alignment purposes. The dotted line indicates ganged tuning capacitors. Usually these are the tuning capacitor of the mixer input tank circuit and the local oscillator tuning capacitor. C3 provides low-impedance coupling between the lower end of the L2 and the grounded end of C2, thus bypassing the decoupling filters in the automatic volume control (AVC) circuit. (Automatic volume, or automatic gain, control is treated later in this chapter.) The rf transformer in the output circuit consists of an untuned high-impedance primary, L3, and a tuned secondary, L4, which resonates with tuning capacitor C5 at the station frequency. The rf bypass capacitor, C6, serves a function similar to that of C3.

First Detector

The first detector, or frequency-converter, section of a superheterodyne receiver is composed of two parts—the oscillator and the mixer. In many receivers, particularly at broadcast frequencies, the same vacuum tube serves both functions, as in the pentagrid converter shown in Fig.11-15. The operation of the tube may be simplified somewhat if both stages (oscillator and mixer) are considered as exerting two different influences on the stream of electrons from cathode to plate. These electrons are influenced by the oscillator stage (grids 1,2 and 4) and also by the station input signal on grid

199

number 3. Thus, coupling between the input signal and the oscillator takes place within the electron stream itself.

There is a tendency for the local oscillator to synchronize with the station frequency signal applied to grid 3. At high frequencies where the two signals have nearly the same frequency, the pentagrid converter is replaced with a mixer tube and a separate oscillator tube. This type of circuit provides frequency stability for local oscillator.

The oscillator stage employs a typical Hartley circuit in which C5 and the oscillator coil make up the tuned circuit. C4 is the trimmer capacitor used for alignment (tracking) purposes. C3 and R2 provide grid-leak bias for the oscillator section of the tube. Grid 1 is the oscillator grid, and grids 2 and 4 serve as the oscillator plate. Grids 2 and 4 are connected together and also serve as a shield for the signal input grid, number 3.

Grid 3 has a variable-mu characteristic and serves as both an amplifier and a mixer grid. The tuned input is made up of L1 and C1, with the parallel trimmer C2. The dotted lines drawn through C1 and C5 indicate that both of these capacitors are ganged on the same shaft (in this example with the preselector tuning capacitor). The plate circuit contains the station frequency and the oscillator frequency signals, both of which are bypassed to ground through the low reactance of C6 and C7. The heterodyne action within the pentagrid converter produces additional frequency components in the plate circuit, one of which is the difference frequency between the oscillator and the station frequency. The difference frequency is the intermediate frequency and is developed across C6 and L2. This signal is coupled to the first i-f amplifier grid through the desired band-pass coupling which is wide enough to include the sideband components associated with the amplitude-modulated signal applied to grid 3 of the pentagrid converter.

The conversion gain in a pentagrid converter is

$$\mu = V_d S_c$$

where V_d is the AC plate resistance with the station rf carrier applied, and S_c is the conversion transconductance (30 percent to 40 percent of the g_m of the pentode amplifier). Conversion gain is the change in plate voltage at the intermediate frequency divided by the change in grid voltage at the rf station frequency for equal changes in plate current at the intermediate frequency. Expressed as a formula

$$\text{conversion gain} = \frac{\text{i-f output volts}}{\text{rf input volts}}$$

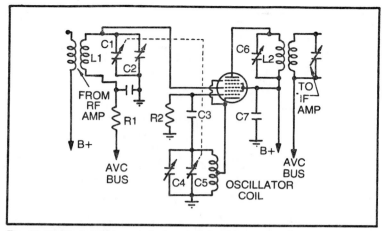

Fig. 11-15. First detector employing a pentagrid converter.

The conversion gain of a typical pentagrid converter used in broadcast receivers ranges between 30 and 80.

Heterodyne Principle

The production of audible beat notes is a phenomenon that is easily demonstrated. For example, if two adjoining piano keys are struck simultaneously, a tone will be produced that rises and decreases in intensity at regular intervals. This action results from the fact that the rarefactions and compressions produced by the vibrating strings will gradually approach a condition in which they reinforce each other at regular intervals of time with an accompanying increase in the intensity of the sound. Likewise, at equal intervals of time, the compressions and rarefactions gradually approach a condition in which they counteract each other, and the intensity is periodically reduced.

This addition and subtraction of the intensities at regular intervals produces *beat frequencies*. The number of beats produced per second is equal to the difference between the two frequencies.

The production of beats in a superheterodyne receiver is somewhat analogous to the action of the piano, except that with the receiver the process is electrical and the frequencies are much higher. Figure 11-16 indicates graphically how the beat frequency (intermediate frequency) is produced when signals of two different frequencies are combined in the mixer tube. The resultant envelope varies in amplitude at the difference frequency, as indicated by the dotted lines.

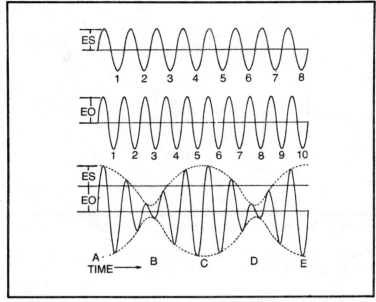

Fig. 11-16. Simplified graphical analysis of the formation of beats.

In this example, one voltage, e_s, has a frequency of 8 cycles per second and the other voltage, e_o, has a frequency of 10 cycles per second. Initially, the amplitudes of the two voltages add at instant A but at instant B the relative phase of e_o has advanced enough to oppose e_s, and the amplitude of the resultant envelope is reduced to a value dependent upon e_s. At instant C the relative phase of e_o has advanced enough to permit the amplitudes to add again. Thus, one cycle of amplitude variation of the envelope takes place in the time interval that e_o needs to gain one cycle over e_s. From Fig. 11-16 it may be seen that e_o gains two cycles in the interval A to E. Therefore, the beat or difference frequency is 2 cycles per second. In the superheterodyne receiver the amplitude of the oscillator signal is designed to be greater than that of any received signal.

I-F Amplifier

The i-f amplifier is a high-gain circuit commonly employing pentode tubes. This amplifier is tuned to the frequency difference between the local oscillator and the incoming rf signal. Pentode tubes are generally employed with one, two, or three stages, depending on the amount of gain needed. As previously stated, all incoming signals are converted to the same frequency by the frequency converter, and the i-f amplifier operates at only one frequency. The tuned circuits, therefore, are permanently adjusted for maximum gain consistent with the desired bandpass and frequency response. These stages operate as class-A voltage amplifiers, and practically all of the selectivity of the superheterodyne receiver is developed by them.

Figure 11-17 shows the first i-f amplifier stage. The minimum bias is established by means of $R_1 C_1$. Automatic volume control can be applied to the grid through the secondary of the preceding coupling transformer.

The output i-f transformer, which couples the plate circuit of this stage to the grid circuit of the second i-f stage, is tuned by means of capacitors C_2 and C_3. Mica or air-trimmer capacitors were used in old-time radios. In newer radios the capacitors are fixed, and the tuning is accomplished by means of a movable powdered-iron core. This method is called *permeability tuning*. In special cases only the secondary is tuned (single tuned). The coils and capacitors are mounted in small metal cans that serve as shields, and provision is made for adjusting the tuning without removing the shield.

The input i-f transformer has a lower coefficient of coupling than he output transformer in some receivers in order to suppress noise from the pentigrid converter. The output i-f transformer is slightly overcoupled with double humps appearing at the upper and lower sideband frequencies. The overall response of the stage is essen-

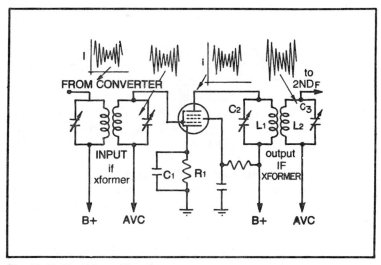

Fig. 11-17. First i-f amplifier stage.

tially flat, and in typical broadcast receivers has a voltage gain of about 200 with a bandpass of 7 to 10 kH and an i-f of about 456 kHz.

The chief characteristic of the double-tuned band-pass coupling is that at frequencies slightly above and slightly below the intermediate frequency, the impedance coupled into the primary by the presence of the secondary is reactive. This cancels some of the reactance existing in the primary, and the primary current increases. Thus the output voltage of the secondary does not fall off, and the response is uniform within the pass band.

Demodulation of Waves

Demodulation, or detection, is the process of recovering the intelligence from a modulated wave. When a radio carrier wave is amplitude-modulated, the intelligence is imposed on the carrier in the form of amplitude variations of the carrier. The demodulator of an amplitude-modulated (AM) wave produces currents or voltages that vary with the amplitude of the wave. Likewise, the frequency-modulation (FM) detector and the phase-modulation (PM) detector change the frequency variations of an FM wave—and the equivalent phase variations of a FM wave—into currents or voltages that vary in amplitude with the frequency or phase of the carrier.

The detector in the receiver must therefore be designed so that it will be sensitive to the type of modulation used at the transmitter, and generally insensitive to any other.

Most collectible radios are designed for amplitude modulation. A clear understanding of the mechanism of AM detection is therefore very important.

AM modulators and demodulators are nonlinear devices. A nonlinear device is one whose current to voltage relationship is *not* a straight line. Because the ratio of current to voltage is not constant, the device has a nonlinear impedance—for example, in one of the electron-tube detectors to be considered later, the average output current is the difference between each successive positive and negative swing of the output signal current, as shown in Fig. 11-18. The average output (signal component) follows the envelope of the incoming modulated wave more or less closely, depending on the shape of the nonlinear curve. Because the envelope of the incoming AM wave contains the desired audio frequency, a nonlinear device demodulates the AM wave.

For an understanding of the difference in the output frequencies of the various detectors, it is necessary to examine the frequencies involved in both modulation and demodulation.

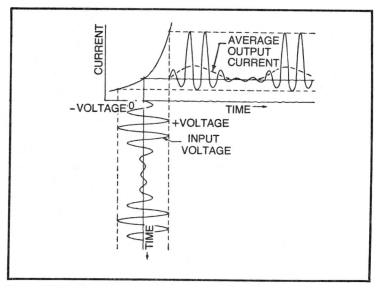

Fig. 11-18. Results of impressing an AM wave on a nonlinear device.

Comparison of Amplitude Modulation and Demodulation

If at the transmitter, an rf carrier and a single-frequency audio-modulating signal of sine waveform are impressed on a linear device, the output waveform from the linear device will contain the same rf and af signal frequencies. The tuned rf amplifiers in the transmitter will amplify the rf carrier but will eliminate for all practical purposes the af component. Under these circumstances, only the carrier will be radiated, and it will be ineffective in carrying the intelligence component.

A very different result is obtained if an rf carrier and a single-frequency audio-modulating signal of sine waveform are impressed on a nonlinear device. In this instance distortion is introduced and, as a result, additional frequencies are produced. In addition to the original frequencies, sum-and-difference frequencies are generated, and a zero-frequency, or DC component, is added. The tuned circuits at the transmitter now respond to the carrier and the upper and lower sidebands. As before, though, the af modulating signal is discriminated against. However, this af component is replaced, or generated, by the demodulator in the receiver.

In the receiver the carrier and the two sidebands are impressed on a second nonlinear device called the demodulator. If the demodulator has an ideal nonlinear curve, it will distort the incoming waveform (the positive halves of the cycle will be different from the negative halves). Therefore, in addition to the rf carrier and the two sidebands, the signal frequency—the difference between the upper sideband and the carrier or the difference between the carrier and the lower sideband—and a zero-frequency, or DC component will be produced. This DC component may be used for automatic volume control.

If the demodulator used in the receiver does not have an ideal nonlinear curve but has a practical realizable curve such as the square-law curve, additional frequencies will be produced. These frequencies will be harmonics of all frequencies present in the input. They are produced because input voltages having larger amplitudes are distorted differently from input voltages having smaller amplitudes. The rf harmonics may be filtered in the output of the demodulator, but the af harmonics are not easily eliminated.

Thus, modulation and demodulation are essentially the same in that the waveform is distorted in each case and new frequencies are produced.

Types of AM Detectors

Detectors are classified according to the shape of their current-voltage (characteristic) curve. If the curve is smooth, as in Fig. 11-18, the detector is called a square-law detector. It is called a square-law detector because, for a first approximation, the output voltage is proportional to the square of the effective input voltage.

If the current voltage curve of the detector is shaped like an obtuse angle, as in Fig. 11-19A, the curve is still nonlinear because of the abrupt change in shape at the knee. Because the detector action takes place on the linear portions of the curve on both sides of the voltage applied to the plate on the next cycle exceeds the potential at which the capacitor holds the cathode (point B), diode current again flows and the capacitor charges up to almost the peak value of the second positive half cycle at point C.

So the voltage across the capacitor follows very nearly the peak value of the applied rf voltage and reproduces the af modulation. The detector output, after rectification and filtering, is a DC voltage that varies at an audio rate, as shown by the solid line in Fig. 11-20E. The curve of the output voltage across the capacitor is shown somewhat jagged. Actually, the rf component of this voltage is negligible and, after amplification, the speech or music orginating at the transmitter is faithfully reproduced.

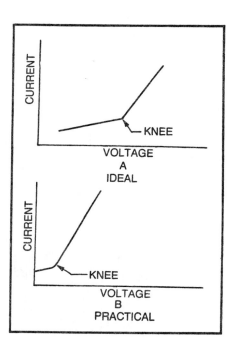

Fig. 11-19. Linear detectors.

The correct choice of R and C₂ (Fig. 11-20A) in the diode-detector circuit is very important if maximum sensitivity and fidelity are to be obtained. The load resistor, R, and the plate resistance of the diode act as a voltage divider to the received signal. Therefore, the load resistance should be high compared with the plate resistance of the diode so that maximum output voltage will be obtained. The value of C2 should be such that the RC time constant is long compared with the time of one rf cycle. This is necessary because the capacitor must maintain the voltage across the load resistor during the time when there is no plate current. Also, the RC time constant must be short compared with the time of one af cycle in order that the capacitor voltage can follow the modulation envelope.

The values of R and C2 therefore place a limit on the highest modulation (audio) frequency that can be detected. Figure 11-20F shows the type of distortion that occurs when the RC time constant is too large. At the higher modulation frequencies, the capacitor does not discharge as rapidly as required, and negative peak clipping of the audio signal results.

The efficiency of rectification in a diode is the ratio of the peak voltage appearing across the load to the peak input signal voltage. The efficiency increases with the size of R compared with the diode

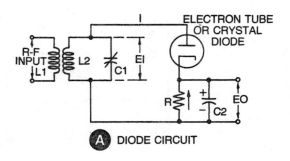

A DIODE CIRCUIT

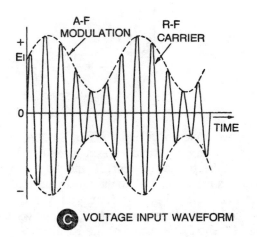

C VOLTAGE INPUT WAVEFORM

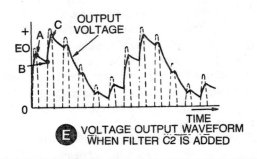

E VOLTAGE OUTPUT WAVEFORM
WHEN FILTER C2 IS ADDED

Fig. 11-20. Diode detector and waveforms.

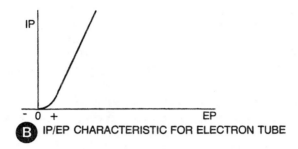

B IP/EP CHARACTERISTIC FOR ELECTRON TUBE

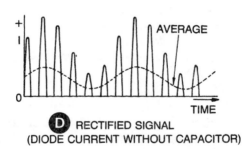

D RECTIFIED SIGNAL
(DIODE CURRENT WITHOUT CAPACITOR)

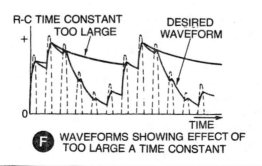

F WAVEFORMS SHOWING EFFECT OF
TOO LARGE A TIME CONSTANT

plate resistance, because R and the diode are in series across the input circuit and their voltages divide in proportion to their resistance. With audio frequencies, a large value of R may be used (of the order of 100,000 ohms), and consequently the efficiency is relatively high (95 percent). When high modulation frequencies are necessary, the value of R must be reduced to keep the RC time constant low enough to follow the envelope. Consequently, the efficiency is reduced.

The diode detector can handle large signals without overloading, and it can provide automatic volume control voltage without extra tubes or special circuits. However, it has the disadvantage of drawing power from the input tuned circuit because the diode and its load form a low-impedance shunt across the circuit.

Consequently, the circuit Q, the sensitivity and the selectivity are reduced. The interelectrode capacitance of the diode detector limits its usefulness at high carrier frequencies, and the bend in the lower portion of current-voltage characteristic indicates that it distorts on weak signals. Therefore, considerable amplification is needed before detection.

Grid-Leak Detector

The grid-leak-detector functions like a diode detector combined with a triode amplifier. It is convenient to consider detection and amplification as two separate functions. In Fig. 11-21A, the grid functions as the diode plate. The values of C_d and R_d must be so chosen that C_d charges during the positive peaks of the incoming signal and discharges during the negative peaks. The time constant of $R_d C_d$ should be long with respect to the rf cycle and short with respect to the af cycle.

An approximate analysis of the waveforms existing in the diode (grid) circuit is shown in Fig. 11-21B. Part 1 shows the input waveform, which is also the waveform in the input tuned circuit. Because rf current i_g flows in only one direction in the grid circuit, part 2 shows a rectified current waveform in this circuit. Part 3 shows the waveform developed across C_d. This audio waveform is produced in the same way as the audio waveform in the diode detector. However, the waveform shown in part 3 is not the output voltage. In the grid-leak detector, the waveform produced across C_d is combined in series with the rf waveform in the tuned circuit to produce the grid-to-cathode waveform shown in part 4.

An approximate analysis of the waveforms existing in the triode plate circuit is shown in Fig. 11-21C. Part 5 is the plate-current waveform, and part 6 is the plate-voltage waveform.

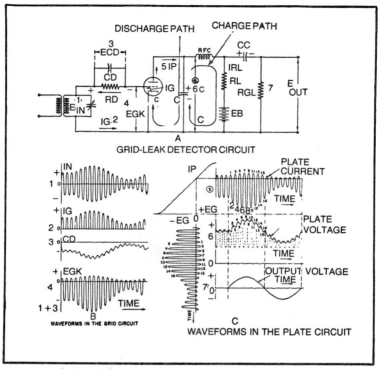

Fig. 11-21. Grid-leak detector and waveforms.

Capacitor C discharges on the positive half cycles of grid input voltage (points 1, 3, 5, 7, 9, 11, 13 and so forth). The discharge path is clockwise through the circuit including the tube and capacitor. The time constant of the discharge path is the product of the effective tube resistance and the capacitance of capacitor C. This time constant is short because the effective tube resistance is low. The increase in plate current is supplied by the capacitor rather than the B + supply, thus preventing any further increase in current through the rf choke and plate load resistor RL. Therefore, any further change in plate and capacitor voltage is limited.

Capacitor C charges up as plate voltage rises on the negative half cycles of rf grid input voltage (Fig. 11-21C, points 2, 4, 6, 8, 10, 12, 14 and so forth). The charging path is clockwise through the circuit containing the capacitor, rf choke, load resistor RL and the B+ supply. The rise in plate voltage is limited by the capacitor charging current that flows through the rf choke and through RL. The plate current decrease is approximately equal to the capacitor charging current so the total current through the rf choke and R_L remains nearly constant, and the plate and capacitor voltage rise is checked.

Positive grid swings cause sufficient grid current flow to produce grid-leak bias. Low plate limits the plate current on no signal in the absence of grid bias. Accordingly, the amplitude of the input signal is limited, since with low plate voltage the cutoff bias is low, and that portion of the input signal that drives the grid voltage below cutoff is lost. The waveform of the voltage across capacitor C is shown by the solid line in part 6 of Fig. 11-21C. The plate voltage ripple is removed by the rf choke (RFC). Part 7 shows the output-voltage waveform. This waveform is the difference between the voltage at the junction of R_L and RFC with respect to the negative terminal of E_b and the voltage across coupling capacitor C_c, which for most practical purposes is a pure DC voltage.

Because the operation of the grid-leak detector depends on a certain amount of grid-current flow, a loading effect is produced which lowers the selectivity of the input circuit. However, the sensitivity of the grid-leak detector is moderately high on low-amplitude signals.

Plate Detector

In a grid-leak-detector the incoming rf signal is detected in the grid circuit and the resultant af signal is amplified in the plate circuit. In a plate detector, the rf signal is first amplified in the plate circuit, and then it is detected in the same circuit.

A plate detector circuit is shown in Fig. 11-22A. The cathode bias resistor, R_1, is chosen so that the grid bias is approximately at cutoff during the time that an input signal of proper strength is applied. Plate current then flows only on the positive swings of grid voltage, during which time average plate current increases. The peak value of the AC input signal is limited to slightly less that the cutoff bias to prevent driving the grid voltage positive on the positive half cycles of the input signal. As a result, no grid current flows at any time in the input cycle, and the detector does not load the input tuned circuit, LC_1.

Cathode bypass capacitor C_2 is large enough to hold the voltage across R_1 steady at the lowest audio frequency to be detected in the plate circuit. C_3 is the demodulation capacitor across which the af component is developed. R_2 is the plate load resistor. The rf choke blocks the rf component from the output. R_2R_3 has a long time

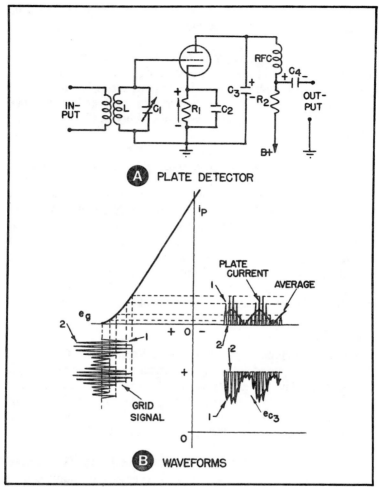

Fig. 11-22. Plate detector and waveforms.

constant with respect to the time for one rf cycle so that C_3 resists any voltage which occurs at the rf rate. R_2C_3 has a short time constant with respect to the time for one cycle so that the capacitor is capable of charging and discharging at the audio rate.

The action of the plate detector may be demonstrated by the use of the i_p-e_g curve in Fig. 11-22B. On the positive half cycle of rf input signal (point 1), the plate voltage falls below the B+ supply because of the increased drop across R_2 and the r f choke. Capacitor C_3 discharges. The discharge current flows clockwise through the circuit including the tube and C rather than the B supply. The drop across R₂ and the rf choke is limited, and the decrease in plate voltage is slight.

On the negative half cycle of rf input signal (point 2) plate current is cut off and plate voltage rises. Capacitor C₃ charges. The charging current flows clockwise around the circuit, including the rf choke, R₂ and the B + supply. The drop across R₂ and the rf choke contributed by the charging current of C₃ checks the rise in plate voltage.

Thus, C₃ resists voltage change at the rf rate. Because C₃R₂ has a short time constant with respect to the lowest af signal, the voltage across C₃ varies at the af rate.

The plate detector has excellent selectivity. Its sensitivity (ratio of af output to rf input) is also greater than that of the diode detector. However, it is inferior to the diode detector in that it is unable to handle strong signals without overloading. Another disadvantage is that the operating bias will vary with the strength of the incoming signal and thus cause distortion unless a means is provided to maintain the signal input at a constant level. This is why AVC or manual rf gain control circuits usually precede the detector.

Second Detector

Most superheterodyne receivers employ a diode as the second detector. This type of detector is practical because of the high gain as well as the high selectivity of the i-f stages. The diode detector has good linearity and can handle large signals without overloading. For reasons of space and economy, the diode detector and first audio amplifier are often included in the same envelope in modern superheterodyne receivers.

A simple diode detector is shown in Fig. 11-23. The rectified voltage appears across R₁, which also serves as the volume control pontentiometer. Capacitor C₂ bypasses the rf component to ground, and C₃ couples the output of the detector to the first audio amplifier stage. The tuned circuit, L₂C₁ is long compared to the time for one i-f cycle but short compared to the time for one af cycle. If the intermediate frequency is 456 kHa, the time for one i-f cycle in microseconds is

$$\frac{1}{0456} = 2.19 \ \mu s$$

If R1 is 250K and C₂ is 100 pF, the time constant in microseconds is $0.25 \times 100 = 25 \ \mu s$

214

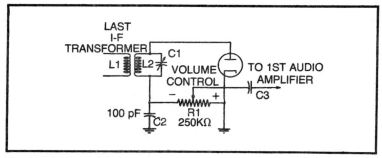

Fig. 11-23. Diode detector.

The demodulation capacitor, C2, discharges through R_1 in one-half the time for one af cycle, 1/2f. The time required to discharge C2, is $5R_1C_2$ seconds. Thus

$$1/2f = \frac{5R}{f}$$

$$= 1/10 \times R1 \times C2$$

$$= \frac{1}{10 \times 0.250 \times 10^6 \times 100 \times 10^{-12}}$$

$$= 103/0.250$$

$$= 4000 \text{ Hz}$$

So the highest audio frequency that C_2 is capable of following without distortion is, in this example, 4000 Hz. In order to increase the response of the diode detector, the time constant of R_1C_2 is reduced, for example, by decreasing R_1 to 100K. The highest audio frequency now becomes

$$f = 1/10 \times R1 \times C2$$

$$= 1/10 \times 0.100 \times 10^6 \times 100 \times 10^{-12}$$

$$= 10^6/10^2$$

$$= 10000 \text{ Hz}$$

Demodulation capacitor C_2 cannot discharge rapidly enough to follow modulation frequencies higher than 10,000 Hz (in this case), and clipping results with all higher audio frequencies.

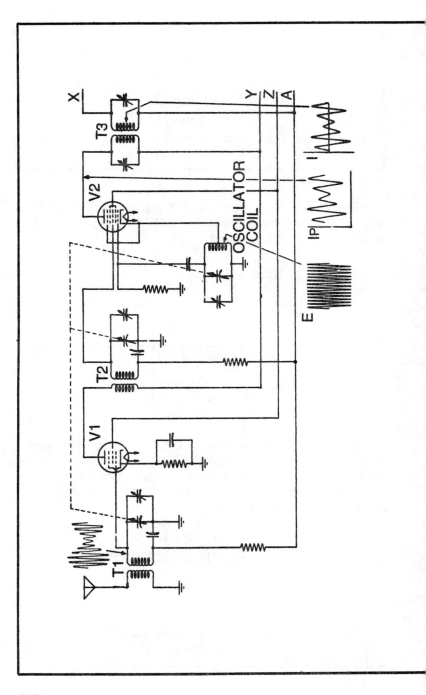

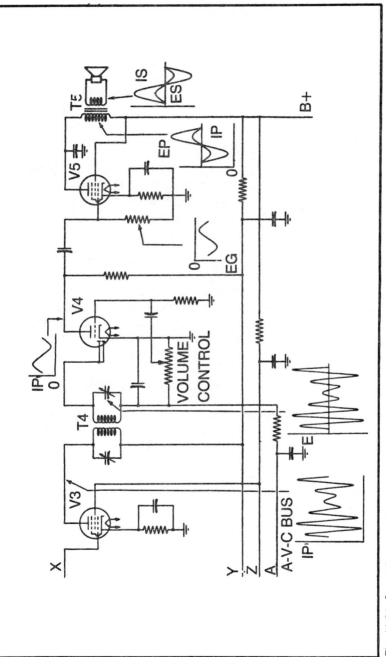

Fig. 11-24. Circuit diagram of a superheterodyne receiver.

217

Circuit of a Superheterodyne Receiver

The complete circuit of a superheterodyne receiver is shown in Fig. 11-24. In this circuit one rf amplifier (preselector) stage is used. Tube V_2, a pentagrid converter, serves both as the mixer tube and oscillator tube. Three tuning capacitors (one each in the preselector, mixer and oscillator stages) are ganged on a common shaft to assure proper tracking. Trimmers are connected in parallel with each capacitor to permit alignment. The oscillator tuning capacitor is smaller than the tuning capacitor in the preselector or the converter stages. The oscillator operates above the station frequency and tracks closely at three points on the dial—the low end, the middle and the high end. The oscillator tuning capacitor split-rotor plates allow closer adjustment for tracking at the low end and at the middle of the band. Shunt trimmer capacity adjustments on the oscillator tuning capacitor provide close tracking of the oscillator at the high end of the band.

Tube V_3 is the i-f amplifier with input and output i-f transformers tuned to the receiver intermediate frequency.

Tube V_4 serves as the second detector and first audio amplifier. Conventional automatic volume control is tapped off at the end of the volume control potentiometer farthest from ground. Plate and screen potentials are obtained from the B+ supply through the corresponding voltage-dropping resistors. The power supply is a conventional full-wave rectifier.

The final stage in the receiver contains a power amplifier; it may be single ended or push-pull. Figure 11-24 shows a complete power amplifier stage containing V_5, associated resistors and capacitors, a transformer and a speaker. The stage operates as a class A amplifier in this case, since it is single ended. If push-pull is used, the stage can operate as class A, AB or B. In any case, the energy is transformer-coupled to the load—the speaker in Fig. 11-24—for better impedance matching.

Appendix

RCA Receiving Tubes
Characteristic Chart

RCA Type	Name	Tube Dimensions	Cathode Type and Rating C.T.	Volts	Amp.	Use	Plate Supply Volts	Grid Bias Volts	Screen Supply Volts	Screen Current Ma	Plate Current Ma	AC Plate Resistance Ohms	Transconductance (Grid-plate) umhos	Amplification Factor	Load (for Stated Power Output) Ohms	Power Output Watts	RCA Type
00-A	Detector Triode	D12	D.C. F	5.0	0.25	Grid-Leak Detector	45	Grid Return to (—)Filament				30000	666	20	—	—	00-A
01-A	Detector★ Amplifier	D12	D.C. F	5.0	0.25	Class A Amplifier	90 / 135	— 4.5 / — 9.0			2.5 / 3.0	11000 / 10000	725 / 800	8.0 / 8.0	—	—	01-A
0Z4	Full-Wave Gas Rectifier	B3	Cold	—	—	Rectifier	Starting-Supply Voltage per Plate, 300 min. peak volts. Peak Plate Current, 200 max. ma. D-C Output Current, 75 max., 30 min. ma. D-C Output Voltage, 300 max. volts.										0Z4
0Z4-G	Full-Wave Gas Rectifier	B1	Cold	—	—	Rectifier											0Z4-G
1A3	HF Diode	B0	H	1.4	0.15	Detector Rectifier	Max. D-C Output Ma., 0.5 Max. Peak Inverse Volts, 330 Max. Peak Plate Ma., 5 Max. Peak Heater-Cathode Volts, 140										1A3
1A4-P	Supercontrol RF Amplifier Pentode	D9	D.C. F	2.0	0.06	Amplifier	For other characteristics, refer to Type 1D5-GP.										1A4-P
1A5-GT	Power Amplifier Pentode	C3	D.C. F	1.4	0.05	Class A Amplifier	85 / 90	— 4.5 / — 4.5	85 / 90	0.7 / 0.8	3.5 / 4.0	300000 / 300000	800 / 850	—	25000 / 25000	0.100 / 0.115	1A5-GT
1A6	Pentagrid Converter @	D9	D.C. F	2.0	0.06	Converter	135 / 180	{— 3.0 min.}	67.5 / 67.5	2.5 / 2.4	1.2 / 1.3	400000 / 500000		Anode-Grid (#2): 180 max. volts, 2.3 ma. Oscillator-Grid (#1) Resistor a. Conversion Transcond., 300 micromhos.			1A6
1A7-GT	Pentagrid Converter @	C3	D.C. F	1.4	0.05	Converter	90	0	45¢	0.7	0.6	600000		Anode-Grid (#2): 90 max. volts, 1.2 ma. Oscillator-Grid (#1) Resistor, 0.2 meg. Conversion Transcond., 250 micromhos.			1A7-GT
1B3-GT/8016	Half-Wave Rectifier	B1a	F	1.25	0.2	Half-Wave Rectifier	Max. Peak Inverse Plate Volts, 40000	Max. Peak Plate Ma., 17				Max. Average Plate Ma., 2 Max. Frequency of Supply Voltage, 300 Kc					1B3-GT/8016
1B4-P	RF Amplifier Pentode	D9	D.C. F	2.0	0.06	Amplifier	For other characteristics, refer to Type 1E5-GP.										1B4-P
1B5/25S	Duplex-Diode Triode	D6	D.C. F	2.0	0.06	Triode Unit as Amplifier	For other characteristics, refer to Type 1H6-G.										1B5/25S
1B7-GT	Pentagrid Converter	C3	D.C. F	1.4	0.10	Converter	90	0	45¢	1.3	1.5	350000		Anode-Grid (#2): 90 max. volts, 1.6 ma. Oscillator-Grid (#1) Resistor, 0.2 meg. Conversion Transcond., 350 micromhos.			1B7-GT
1C5-GT	Power Amplifier Pentode	C3	D.C. F	1.4	0.10	Class A Amplifier	83 / 90	— 7.0 / — 7.5	83 / 90	1.6 / 1.6	7.0 / 7.5	110000 / 115000	1500 / 1550	—	9000 / 8000	0.20 / 0.24	1C5-GT
1C6	Pentagrid Converter @	D9	D.C. F	2.0	0.12	Converter	For other characteristics, refer to Type 1C7-G.										1C6
1C7-G	Pentagrid Converter @	D8	D.C. F	2.0	0.12	Converter	135 / 180	— 3.0 / — 3.0	67.5 / 67.5	2.5 / 2.0	1.3 / 1.5	600000 / 700000		Anode-Grid (#2): 180 max. volts, 4.0 ma. Oscillator-Grid (#1) Resistor. Conversion Transcond., 325 micromhos.			1C7-G
1D5-GP	Supercontrol RF Amplifier Pentode	D9	D.C. F	2.0	0.06	Class A Amplifier	90 / 180	{— 3.0 min.}	67.5 / —67.5	0.9 / 0.8	2.2 / 2.3	600000 / 1.0¢	720 / 750		—	—	1D5-GP

Reproduced with permission of RCA Corporation.

	Tetrode																
1D7-G	Pentagrid Converter ⊕	D8	D.C. F	2.0	0.06	Converter	For other characteristics, refer to Type 1A6.										1D7-G
1D8-GT	Diode-Triode-Power Amplifier Pentode	C3	D.C. F	1.4	0.10	Pentode Unit as Class A Amplifier	45 90	− 4.5 − 9.0	45 90	0.3 1.0	1.6 5.0	300000 200000	650 925	—	20000 12000	0.035 0.200	1D8-GT
						Triode Unit as Class A Amplifier	45 90	0 0	—	—	0.3 1.1	77000 43500	325 575	25 25	—	—	
1E5-GP	RF Amplifier Pentode	D8	D.C. F	2.0	0.06	Class A Amplifier	90 180	− 3.0 − 3.0	67.5 67.5	0.7 0.6	1.6 1.7	1.0§ 1.3§	600 650	—	—	—	1E5-GP
1E7-G	Twin-Pentode Power Amplifier	D3	D.C. F	2.0	0.24	Class A Amplifier	135	− 7.5	135	—	Power Output is for one tube at stated plate-to-plate load.				24000	0.575	1E7-G
1F4	Power Amplifier Pentode	D12	D.C. F	2.0	0.12	Amplifier	For other characteristics, refer to Type 1F5-G.										1F4
1F5-G	Power Amplifier Pentode	D10	D.C. F	2.0	0.12	Class A Amplifier	90 135	− 3.0 − 4.5	90 135	1.1 2.4	4.0 8.0	240000 200000	1400 1700	—	20000 16000	0.11 0.31	1F5-G
1F6	Duplex-Diode Pentode	D9	D.C. F	2.0	0.06	Pentode Unit as Amplifier	For other characteristics, refer to Type 1F7-G.										1F6
1F7-G	Duplex-Diode Pentode	D8	D.C. F	2.0	0.06	Pentode Unit as RF Amplifier	180	− 1.5	67.5	0.7	2.2	1.0§	650	—	—	—	1F7-G
						Pentode Unit as AF Amplifier	135⌘	− 2.0	Screen Supply, 135 volts applied through 0.8-megohm resistor. Grid Resistor,** 1.0 megohm. Voltage Gain, 46.								
1G4-GT	Detector Amplifier Triode	C3	D.C. F	1.4	0.05	Class A Amplifier	90	− 6.0	—	—	2.3	10700	825	8.8	—	—	1G4-GT
1G5-G	Power Amplifier Pentode	D10	D.C. F	2.0	0.12	Class A Amplifier	90 135	− 6.0 −13.5	90 135	2.5 2.5	8.5 8.7	133000 160000	1500 1550	—	8500 9000	0.25 0.55	1G5-G
1G6-GT	Twin-Triode Amplifier	C3	D.C. F	1.4	0.10	Class B Amplifier	90	0	—	—	Power Output is for one tube at stated plate-to-plate load				12000	0.350	1G6-GT
1H4-G	Detector★ Amplifier	D3	D.C. F	2.0	0.06	Class A Amplifier	90 135 180	− 4.5 − 9.0 −13.5	—	—	2.5 3.0 3.1	11000 10300 10300	850 900 900	9.3 9.3 9.3	—	—	1H4-G
						Class B Amplifier	157.5	−15.0	—	—	1.0♦	—	—	—	8000	2.1†	
1H5-GT	Diode High-Mu Triode	C3	D.C. F	1.4	0.05	Triode Unit as Class A Amplifier	90	0	—	—	0.15	240000	275	65	—	—	1H5-GT
1H6-G	Duplex-Diode Triode	D3	D.C. F	2.0	0.06	Triode Unit as Class A Amplifier	135	− 3.0	—	—	0.8	35000	575	20	—	—	1H6-G
1J5-G	Power Amplifier Pentode	D10	D.C. F	2.0	0.12	Class A Amplifier	135	−16.5	135	2.0	7.0	105000	950	—	13500	0.45	1J5-G
1J6-GT	Twin-Triode Amplifier	C5b	D.C. F	2.0	0.24	Class B Amplifier	135 135	0 − 3.0	—	—	Power Output is for one tube at stated plate-to-plate load				10000 10000	2.2 2.0	1J6-GT
1L4	RF Amplifier Pentode	B0	D.C. F	1.4	0.05	Class A Amplifier	90 90	0 0	67.5 90	1.2 2.0	2.9 4.5	600000 260000	925 1025	—	—	—	1L4
1LA4	Power Amplifier Pentode	B5	D.C. F	1.4	0.05	Amplifier	For other characteristics, refer to Type 1A5-GT.										1LA4
1LA6	Pentagrid Converter	B5	D.C. F	1.4	0.05	Converter	90	0	45♦	0.6	0.55	750000	Anode-Grid (⊕2) 90 max volts, 1.2 ma Oscillator Grid (⊕1) Resistor, 0.2 meg. Conversion Transcond., 250 micromhos				1LA6

Reproduced with permission of RCA Corporation.

RCA Type	Name	Tube Dimensions	Cathode Type and Rating			Use	Plate Supply Volts	Grid Bias Volts	Screen Supply Volts	Screen Current Ma.	Plate Current Ma.	AC Plate Resistance Ohms	Transconductance (Grid-plate) μmhos	Amplification Factor	Load for Stated Power Output Ohms	Power Output Watts	RCA Type
			C.T.	Volts	Amp.	Values to right give operating conditions and characteristics for indicated typical use											
1LB4	Power Amplifier Pentode	B5	D.C. F	1.4	0.05	Class A Amplifier	For other characteristics, refer to Pentode Unit of Type 1D8-GT.										1LB4
1LC5	RF Amplifier Pentode	B5	D.C. F	1.4	0.05	Class A Amplifier	45 / 90	0 / 0	45 / 45	0.35 / 0.30	1.10 / 1.15	700000 / 1.5§	750 / 775	—	—	—	1LC5
1LC6	Pentagrid Converter	B5	D.C. F	1.4	0.05	Converter	45 / 90	0 / 0	35 / 35	0.75 / 0.70	0.70 / 0.75	300000 / 300000	Anode-Grid (#2): 45 max. volts, 1.4 ma. Oscillator-Grid (#1) Resistor, 1.0 meg. Conversion Transcond.. 275 micromhos.				1LC6
1LD5	Diode-Pentode	B5	D.C. F	1.4	0.05	Pentode Unit as Class A Amplifier	Plate Supply, 90 volts applied through 5.6 meg. resistor. Screen Supply, 90 volts applied through 1 meg. resistor. Grid Resistor, 10 megohms. Voltage Gain, 101 approx.										1LD5
1LE3	Detector Amplifier Triode	B5	F	1.4	0.05	Class A Amplifier	90 / 90	0 / -3	— / —	— / —	4.5 / 1.4	11200 / 19000	1300 / 760	14.5 / 14.5	—	—	1LE3
1LH4	Diode High-Mu Triode	B5	D.C. F	1.4	0.05	Triode Unit as Class A Amplifier	For other characteristics, refer to Type 1H5-GT.										1LH4
1LN5	RF Amplifier Pentode	B5	D.C. F	1.4	0.05	Class A Amplifier	90	0	90	0.35	1.6	1.1§	800	—	—	—	1LN5
1N5-GT	RF Amplifier Pentode	C3	D.C. F	1.4	0.05	Class A Amplifier	90	0	90	0.3	1.2	1.5§	750	—	—	—	1N5-GT
1N6-G	Diode—Power Amplifier Pentode	D1	D.C. F	1.4	0.05	Pentode Unit as Class A Amplifier	90	-4.5	90	0.7	3.4	300000	800	—	25000	0.1	1N6-G
1P5-GT	Supercontrol RF Amplifier Pentode	C3	D.C. F	1.4	0.05	Class A Amplifier	90	0	90	0.7	2.3	800000	750	—	—	—	1P5-GT
1Q5-GT	Beam Power Amplifier	C3	D.C. F	1.4	0.1	Class A Amplifier	110	-6.6	110	1.4	10.0	100000	2200	—	8000	0.40	1Q5-GT
1R5	Pentagrid Converter▲	B0	D.C. F	1.4	0.05	Converter	45 / 90	0 / 0	45 / 67.5	1.9 / 3.2	0.7 / 1.6	600000 / 600000	Grid #1 Resistor, 100000 ohms. Conversion Transcond., 300 micromhos.				1R5
1S4	Power Amplifier Pentode	B0	D.C. F	1.4	0.1	Class A Amplifier	45 / 90	-4.5 / -7.0	45 / 67.5	0.8 / 1.4	3.8 / 7.4	100000 / 100000	1250 / 1575	—	8000 / 8000	0.065 / 0.27	1S4
1S5	Diode-Pentode	B0	D.C. F	1.4	0.05	Pentode Unit as AF Amplifier	Plate Supply, 90 volts applied through 1 meg. resistor. Screen Supply, 90 volts applied through 3 meg. resistor. Grid Bias, 0 volts. Grid Resistor, 10 megohms. Voltage Gain, 50 approx.										1S5
1T4	Super-Control RF Amplifier Pentode	B0	D.C. F	1.4	0.05	Class A Amplifier	45 / 90	0 / 0	45 / 67.5	0.7 / 1.4	1.7 / 3.5	350000 / 500000	700 / 900	—	—	—	1T4
1T5-GT	Beam Power Amplifier	C3	D.C. F	1.4	0.05	Class A Amplifier	90	-6.0	90	0.8	6.5	—	1150	—	14000	0.17	1T5-GT
1U4	RF Amplifier Pentode	B0	D.C. F	1.4	0.05	Class A Amplifier	90	0	90	0.45	1.6	1.5§	900	—	—	—	1U4
1U5	Diode-Pentode	B0	D.C. F	1.4	0.05	Pentode Unit as Class A Amplifier	Plate Supply, 90 volts applied through 1 meg. resistor. Screen Supply, 90 volts applied through 3.3 meg. resistor. Grid Bias, 0 volts. Grid Resistor, 10 megohms. Voltage Gain, 66 approx.										1U5
1-v	Half-Wave Rectifier	D5	H	6.3	0.3	With Capacitive-Input Filter	Max. A-C Plate Volts (RMS), 325 Min. Total Effective Plate-Supply Impedance: Up to 117 volts, 0 ohms; at 150 volts, 30 ohms; at 325 volts, 75 ohms. Max. D-C Output Ma., 45										1-v

Type	Description	Socket	f	Volts	Amps	Class / Mode	Plate V	Grid V	Screen V	Screen mA	Plate mA	Plate Res. (ohms)	Gm (μmhos)	Load (ohms) / μ	Power (W)	Notes
2A5	Power Amplifier Pentode	D12	H	2.5	1.75	Push-Pull Class AB₁ Amplifier	300 / 300	Cath. Bias, 780 ohms / −62 volts, fixed bias			80.0♦ / 80.0♦			5000 / 3000	10.0† / 15.0†	For other characteristics, refer to Type 6F6-G.
2A6	Duplex-Diode High-Mu Triode	D9	H	2.5	0.8	Amplifier										For other characteristics, refer to Type 6SQ7.
2A7	Pentagrid Converter ⊛	D9	H	2.5	0.8	Converter										For other characteristics, refer to Type 6A8.
2B7	Duplex-Diode Pentode	D9	H	2.5	0.8	Pentode Unit as Amplifier										For other characteristics, refer to Type 6B8-G.
2E5	Electron-Ray Tube	D5	H	2.5	0.8	Visual Indicator										For other characteristics, refer to Type 6E5.
3A8-GT	Diode-Triode RF Amplifier Pentode	C8a	D.C. / F	1.4 / 2.8	0.1 / 0.05	Triode Unit as Class A Amplifier	90	0	—		0.2	200000	325	65	—	For other characteristics, refer to Type 3Q5-GT.
						Pentode Unit as Class A Amplifier	90	0	90	0.5	1.5	800000	750	—	—	
3LF4	Beam Power Amplifier Pentode	B5	D.C. / F	1.4 / 2.8	0.1 / 0.05	Class A Amplifier										For other characteristics, refer to Type 3Q5-GT.
3Q4	Power Amplifier Pentode	B0	D.C. / F	1.4 / 2.8	0.1 / 0.05	Class A Amplifier										For other characteristics, refer to Type 3V4.
3Q5-GT	Beam Power Amplifier	C3	D.C. / F	1.4 / 2.8	0.1 / 0.05	Class A Amplifier	110 / 110	−6.6 / −6.6	110 / 110		10.0 / 8.5	100000 / 110000	2200 / 2000	8000 / 8000	0.40 / 0.33	
3S4	Power Amplifier Pentode	B0	D.C. / F	1.4 / 2.8	0.1 / 0.05	Class A Amplifier	90 / 90	−7 / −7	67.5 / 67.5		7.4 / 6.1	100000 / 100000	1575 / 1425	8000 / 8000	0.27 / 0.235	
3V4	Power Amplifier Pentode	B0	D.C. / F	1.4 / 2.8	0.1 / 0.05	Class A Amplifier	90 / 90	−4.5 / −4.5	90 / 90		9.5 / 7.7	100000 / 120000	2150 / 2000	10000 / 10000	0.27 / 0.24	
5T4	Full-Wave Rectifier	D7	F	5.0	2.0	With Capacitive-Input Filter										Max. A-C Volts per Plate (RMS), 450; Max. Peak Inverse Volts, 1550; Max. D-C Output Ma., 225; Max. Peak Plate Ma., 675. Min. Total Effect. Supply Imped. per Plate, 150 ohms.
						With Inductive-Input Filter										Max. A-C Volts per Plate (RMS), 550; Max. Peak Inverse Volts, 1550; Max. D-C Output Ma., 225; Max. Peak Plate Ma., 675. Min. Value of Input Choke, 3 henries.
5TP4	Projection Kinescope	H1	H	6.3	0.6	Picture Reproduction With Reflective Optical System										Focus: Electrostatic. Deflection: Magnetic. Deflection Angle: 50°. Phosphor: No. 4. Picture Size: 18" x 24". Anode-No. 2 Volts, 27000 (max.); Anode-No. 1 Volts for Focus, 4300 to 5400 (6000 max.); Grd-No. 2 Volts, 200 (350 max.); Grd-No. 1 Volts for Visual Cutoff, −42 to −98. Anode-No. 2 Current Range, 100 to 200 microamperes; Anode-No. 1 Current, 75 microamperes (max.); Grd-No. 1 Current, −15 to +15 microamperes.
5U4-G	Full-Wave Rectifier	E2	F	5.0	3.0	With Capacitive-Input Filter										Max. A-C Volts per Plate (RMS), 450; Max. Peak Inverse Volts, 1550; Max. D-C Output Ma., 225; Max. Peak Plate Ma., 675. Min. Total Effect. Supply Imped. per Plate, 75 ohms.
						With Inductive-Input Filter										Max. A-C Volts per Plate (RMS), 550; Max. Peak Inverse Volts, 1550; Max. D-C Output Ma., 225; Max. Peak Plate Ma., 675. Min. Value of Input Choke, 3 henries.
5V4-G	Full-Wave Rectifier	D10	H	5.0	2.0	With Capacitive-Input Filter										Max. A-C Volts per Plate (RMS), 375; Max. Peak Inverse Volts, 1400; Max. D-C Output Ma., 175; Max. Peak Plate Ma., 525. Min. Total Effect. Supply Imped. per Plate, 100 ohms.
						With Inductive-Input Filter										Max. A-C Volts per Plate (RMS), 500; Max. Peak Inverse Volts, 1400; Max. D-C Output Ma., 175; Max. Peak Plate Ma., 525. Min. Value of Input Choke, 4 henries.
5W4	Full-Wave Rectifier	C2	F	5.0		With Capacitive-Input Filter										Max. A-C Volts per Plate (RMS), 350; Max. Peak Inverse Volts, 1400; Max. D-C Output Ma., 100; Max. Peak Plate Ma., 300. Min. Total Effect. Supply Imped. per Plate, 50 ohms.
5W4-GT	Full-Wave Rectifiers	C7	F	5.0	1.5	With Inductive-Input Filter										Max. A-C Volts per Plate (RMS), 500; Max. Peak Inverse Volts, 1400; Max. D-C Output Ma., 100; Max. Peak Plate Ma., 300. Min. Value of Input Choke, 6 henries.

RCA Type	Name	Tube Dimensions	C.T.	Volts	Amp.	Use	Plate Supply Volts	Grid Bias Volts	Screen Supply Volts	Screen Current Ma.	Plate Current Ma.	AC Plate Resistance Ohms	Transconductance (Grid-plate) μmhos	Amplification Factor	Load for Stated Power Output Ohms	Power Output Watts	RCA Type
5X4-G	Full-Wave Rectifier	E2		5.0	3.0		For other ratings, refer to Type 5U4-G.										5X4-G
5Y3-GT	Full-Wave Rectifier	C7	F	5.0	2.0	With Capacitive-Input Filter	Max. A-C Volts per Plate (RMS), 350 Max. D-C Output Ma., 125 Max. Peak Plate Ma., 375					Min. Total Effect. Supply Imped. per Plate, 50 ohms					5Y3-GT
						With Inductive-Input Filter	Max. A-C Volts per Plate (RMS), 500 Max. D-C Output Ma., 125 Max. Peak Plate Ma., 375					Min. Value of Input Choke, 5 henries					
5Y4-G	Full-Wave Rectifier	D10	F	5.0	2.0		For other ratings, refer to Type 5Y3-GT.										5Y4-G
5Z3	Full-Wave Rectifier	E3	F	5.0	3.0		For other ratings, refer to Type 5U4-G.										5Z3
5Z4	Full-Wave Rectifier	C2	H	5.0	2.0	With Capacitive-Input Filter	Max. A-C Volts per Plate (RMS), 350 Max. D-C Output Ma., 125 Max. Peak Plate Ma., 375					Min. Total Effect. Supply Imped. per Plate, 50 ohms					5Z4
						With Inductive-Input Filter	Max. A-C Volts per Plate (RMS), 500 Max. D-C Output Ma., 125 Max. Peak Plate Ma., 375					Min. Value of Input Choke, 5 henries					
6A3	Power Amplifier Triode	E3	F	6.3	1.0	Amplifier	For other characteristics, refer to Type 6B4-G.										6A3
6A4/LA	Power Amplifier Pentode	D12	F	6.3	0.3	Class A Amplifier	100 / 180	−6.5 / −12.0	100 / 180	1.6 / 3.9	9.0 / 22.0	83250 / 45500	1200 / 2200		11000 / 8000	0.31 / 1.40	6A4/LA
6A6	Twin-Triode Amplifier	D12	H	6.3	0.8	Amplifier	For other characteristics, refer to Type 6N7-GT.										6A6
6A7	Pentagrid Converter ⊕	D9	H	6.3	0.3	Converter	For other characteristics, refer to Type 6A8.										6A7
6A7S	Pentagrid Converter ⊕	D9	H	6.3	0.3	Converter	For other characteristics, refer to Type 6A8.										6A7S
6A8 / 6A8-G / 6A8-GT	Pentagrid Converters ⊕	C1 / D8 / C3	H	6.3	0.3	Converter	100 / 250	−1.5 / −3.0	50 / 100	1.3 / 2.7	1.1 / 3.5	600000 / 360000	Anode-Grid (#2): 250 v. max. volts. 4.0 ma. Oscillator-Grid (#1) Resistor = Conversion Transcond., 550 micromhos.				6A8 / 6A8-G / 6A8-GT
6AB5/6N5	Electron-Ray Tube	D4	H	6.3	0.15	Visual Indicator	Plate & Target Supply = 135 volts. Triode Plate Resistor = 0.25 meg. Target Current = 2.0 ma. Grid Bias, −10.0 volts; Shadow Angle, 0°; Plate Current, 0.5 ma.					Plate & Target Supply = 135 volts. Triode Plate Resistor = 1.0 meg. Target Current = 1.9 ma. Grid Bias, −15.5 volts; Shadow Angle, 0°. Bias, 0 volts; Angle 90°; Plate Current, 0.13 ma.					6AB5/6N5
6AB7/1853	Television Amplifier Pentode	E3	H	6.3	0.45	Class A Amplifier	300	−3.0	200	3.2	12.5	700000	5000				6AB7/1853
6AC5-GT	High-Mu Power Amplifier Triode	C3	H	6.3	0.4	Class B Amplifier	250	0			5.0†				10000	8.0†	6AC5-GT
						Dynamic-Coupled Amplifier With 76 Driver	250	Bias for both 6AC5-GT and 76 is developed in coupling circuit. Average Plate Current of Driver = 5.5 milliamperes. Average Plate Current of 6AC5-GT = 32 milliamperes.							7000	3.7	
6AC7/1852	Television Amplifier Pentode	E3	H	6.3	0.45	Class A Amplifier	300	Cath. Bias	150	2.5	10.0	1.0§	9000	Cathode-Bias Resistor, 160 ohms			6AC7/1852

Reproduced with permission of RCA Corporation

Type	Name	Use	Ref.	H	Heater Volts	Heater Amp	Plate V	Grid V	Screen V	Screen ma	Plate ma	Plate Res (ohms)	Transconductance (µmhos)	Amp Factor	Power Output (W)	Type
6AD6-G	Electron-Ray Tube Twin Indicator Type	Visual Indicator	8a	H	6.3	0.15	[see note a]									6AD6-G
6AD7-G	Triode-Power Amplifier Pentode.	Triode Unit as Class A Amplifier	D10	H	6.3	0.85	250	−25.0	—	—	3.7	19000	325	6	—	6AD7-G
		Pentode Unit as Class A Amplifier					250	−16.5	250	6.5	34.0	80000	2500	—	3.2	
		Pentode Unit With 6F6-G as Push-Pull Class AB Amplifier					375	Cathode-Bias Resistor, 470 ohms♦	250	6.7♦	41.0♦	—	—	—	9.0†	
6AE5-GT	Amplifier Triode	Class A Amplifier	C3	H	6.3	0.3	95	−15.0	—	—	7.0	3500	1200	4.2	—	6AE5-GT
6AE6-G	Twin-Plate Control Tube	Remote-Cutoff Triode	D3	H	6.3	0.15	250 / 250	−1.5 / −35.0	—	—	6.5 / 0.01	25000	1000	25	—	6AE6-G
		Remote-Cutoff Triode					250 / 250	−1.5 / −9.5	—	—	4.5 / 0.01	35000	950	33	—	
6AE7-GT	Twin-Input Triode Amplifier	Class A Amp.▲▲	C3	H	6.3	0.5	250	−13.5	—	—	10.0	4650	3000	14	—	6AE7-GT
		Driver For Push-Pull 6AC5-GT In Dynamic-Coupled Amplifier					250	[see note b]	—	—	—	—	—	—	9.5	
6AF6-G	Electron-Ray Tube Twin Indicator Type	Visual Indicator	B2	H	6.3	0.15	[see note c]									6AF6-G
6AG5	RF Amplifier Pentode	As Pentode Class A Amplifier	B0	H	6.3	0.3	100 / 150	Cath. Bias	—	1.6 / 2.0	5.5 / 7.0	300000 / 800000	4750 / 5000	—	Cath. Bias Res. 100 ohms / Cath. Bias Res. 200 ohms	6AG5
		As Triode□					180 / 250	Cath. Bias	—	—	7.0 / 5.5	7900 / 11000	5700 / 3800	—	Cath. Bias Res. 350 ohms / Cath. Bias Res. 825 ohms	
6AG7	Video Power Amplifier Pentode	Class A Amplifier	C0	H	6.3	0.65	300	Cath. Bias −2.0	125	7.0	28.0	[see note d]				6AG7
6AK6	Power Amplifier Pentode	Class A Amplifier	D0	H	6.3	0.15	180	−9.0	180	2.5	15	200000	2300	—	1.1	6AK6
6AL5	Twin Diode	Detector Rectifier	A1	H	6.3	0.3	[see note e]									6AL5
6AQ5	Beam Power Amplifier	Single Tube Class A Amplifier	B1a	H	6.3	0.45	180 / 250	−8.5 / −12.5	180 / 250	3.0 / 4.5	29.0 / 45.0	58000 / 52000	3700 / 4100	—	2.0 / 4.5	6AQ5
		Push-Pull Class AB Amplifier					250	−15.0	250	5.0♦	70.0♦	—	—	—	10.0†	
6AQ6	Duplex-Diode High-Mu Triode	Triode Unit as Class A Amplifier	B0	H	6.3	0.15	100 / 250	−1.0 / −3.0	—	—	0.8 / 1.0	61000 / 58000	1150 / 1200	70 / 70	—	6AQ6
6AT6	Duplex-Diode High-Mu Triode	Triode Unit as Class A Amplifier	B0	H	6.3	0.3	100 / 250	−1.0 / −3.0	—	—	0.8 / 1.0	54000 / 58000	1300 / 1200	70 / 70	—	6AT6
6AU6	RF Amplifier Pentode	Class A Amplifier	B0	H	6.3	0.3	100 / 150	−1.0 / −1.0	100 / 150	2.0 / 4.3	5.2 / 10.8	500000 / 1.0†(megohm)	3900 / 5200	—	—	6AU6

Notes:

a. 6AD6-G: Target Voltage, 100 volts. Control-Electrode Voltage, 45 volts; Angle, 0°; Shadow Angle, 135°; Target Current, 0.8 ma. Control-Electrode Voltage, −23 volts; Angle, 0°; Shadow Angle, 135°; Target Current, 1.5 ma. Target Voltage, 150 volts. Control-Electrode Voltage, −50 volts; Angle, 0°; Shadow Angle, 135°; Target Current, 3 ma. Target Voltage, 150 volts. Control-Electrode Voltage, 75 volts; Angle, 0°; Target Current, 1.2 ma.

b. 6AE7-GT: Bias for both 6AC5-GT and 6AE7-GT developed in coupling circuit. Zero-Signal Plate Current of 6AE7-GT = 10 milliamperes. Zero-Signal Plate Current of 6AC5-GT = 64 milliamperes. Power Output is for two 6AC5-GT at stated plate-to-plate load.

c. 6AF6-G: Target Voltage, 125 volts. Control-Electrode Voltage, 0 volts; Angle, 0°; Shadow Angle, 90°; Target Current, 0.65 ma. Control-Electrode Voltage, 0 volts; Shadow Angle, 95°; Target Current, ... Target Voltage, 250 volts. Control-Electrode Voltage, 0 volts; Shadow Angle, 95°; Target Current, 2.2 ma. Control-Electrode Voltage, 160 volts; Angle, 0°.

d. 6AG7: Cathode-Bias Resistor, 57 ohms. Load Resistance, 3500 ohms. Peak-to-Peak Volts Output, 140 approx.

e. 6AL5: Max. Peak Inverse Volts, 420. Max. Peak Plate Ma. per Plate, 54. Max. D-C Output Ma. per Plate, 9. Max. Peak Heater-Cathode Volts, 330.

Reproduced with permission of RCA Corporation.

Type	Name	Tube Dimensions	C.T.	Volts	Amp.	Use	Plate Supply Volts	Grid Bias Volts	Screen Supply Volts	Screen Current Ma.	Plate Current Ma.	AC Plate Resistance Ohms	Transconductance (Grid-plate) μmhos	Amplification Factor	Load for Stated Power Output Ohms	Power Output Watts	Type
6AV6	Twin-Diode High-Mu Triode	B0	H	6.3	0.3	Triode Unit as Class A Amplifier	100 / 250	−1.0 / −2.0			0.5 / 1.2	80000 / 62500	1250 / 1600	100 / 100			6AV6
6B4-G	Power Amplifier Triode	E2	F	6.3	1.0	Class A Amplifier / Push-Pull Class AB, Amplifier	250 / 325 / 325	−45.0 / Cath. Bias, 850 ohms◆ / −68 volts, fixed bias			60.0 / 80.0◆ / 80.0◆	800 / —	5250 / —	4.2	2500 / 5000 / 3000	3.20 / 10.0† / 15.0†	6B4-G
6B5	Direct-Coupled Power Amplifier	D12	H	6.3	0.8	Class A Amplifier	For other characteristics, refer to Type 6N6-G.										6B5
6B6-G	Duplex-Diode High-Mu Triode	D6	H	6.3	0.3	Triode Unit as Amplifier	For other characteristics, refer to Type 6SQ7.										6B6-G
6B7	Duplex-Diode Pentode	D9	H	6.3	0.3	Pentode Unit as Amplifier	For other characteristics, refer to Type 6B8-G.										6B7
6B7S	Duplex-Diode Pentode	D9	H	6.3	0.3	Pentode Unit as Amplifier	For other characteristics, refer to Type 6B8-G.										6B7S
6B8	Duplex-Diode Pentode	C1	H	6.3	0.3	Pentode Unit as Amplifier	For other characteristics, refer to Type 12C8.										6B8
6B8-G	Duplex-Diode Pentode	D8	H	6.3	0.3	Pentode Unit as RF Amplifier / Pentode Unit as AF Amplifier	100 / 250 / 90× / 300×	−3.0 / −3.0 / Cath. Bias, 3500 ohms. / Cath. Bias, 1600 ohms.	100 / 125	1.7 / 2.3	5.8 / 9.0	300000 / 600000	950 / 1125	Screen Resistor = 1.1 meg. Grid Resistor = 0.5 megohm. Screen Resistor = 1.2 meg.	Gain per stage = 55 / Gain per stage = 79		6B8-G
6BA6	RF Amplifier Pentode	D8	H	6.3	0.3	Class A Amplifier	100 / 250	Cath. Bias. / Cath. Bias	100 / 100	4.4 / 4.2	10.8 / 11.0	250000 / 1.0	4300 / 4400	Cath. Bias Res., 68 ohms / C'th. Bias Res., 68 ohms			6BA6
6BE6	Pentagrid Converter▲	D0	H	6.3	0.3	Converter	100 / 250	−1.5 / −1.5	100 / 100	8.0 / 7.8	2.8 / 3.0	500000 / 1.0§	Grid #1 Resistor, 20000 ohms Conversion Transcond., 475 micromhos				6BE6
6BF6	Duplex-Diode Triode	D0	H	6.3	0.3	Triode Unit as Class A Amplifier	For other characteristics, refer to Type 6SR7.										6BF6
6BG6-G	Beam Power Amplifier	F1	H	6.3	0.9	Deflection Amplifier in Television Equipment	Max. Ratings: D-C Plate Volts, 500 D-C Plate Current, 100 ma. Plate Dissipation, 20 watts / Typical Operation: D-C Plate and Grid #2 Supply Volts, 400 D-C Plate Current, 70 ma.										6BG6-G
6BH6	Sharp-Cutoff Pentode	D0	H	6.3	0.15	Class A Amplifier	100 / 250	−1.0 / −1.0	100 / 150	1.4 / 2.9	3.6 / 7.4	700000 / 1.4§	3400 / 4600				6BH6
6BJ6	RF Amplifier Pentode	D0	H	6.3	0.15	Class A Amplifier	100 / 250	−1.0 / −1.0	100 / 100	3.5 / 3.3	9.0 / 9.2	250000 / 1.3§	3650 / 3800				6BJ6
6C4	HF Power Triode	D0	H	6.3	0.15	Class A Amplifier / Class C Amplifier	100 / 250 / 300	0 / −8.5 / −27.0			11.8 / 10.5 / 25.0	6250 / 7700	3100 / 2200	19.5 / 17		5.5	6C4
							Grid Current, 7 ma. Driving Power, 0.35 watt										
6C5	Medium-Mu Triodes	B3	H	6.3	0.3	Class A Amplifier	250	−8.0			8.0	10000	2000	20			6C5
6C5-GT		C3				Bias Detector	250	−17.0 approx.		Cath. Bias, 6400 ohms. / Cath. Bias, 5300 ohms.				Grid Resistor,** 0.25 megohm. Plate current to be adjusted to 0.2 milliampere with no signal.		Gain per stage = 11 / Gain per stage = 13	6C5-GT

Reproduced with permission of RCA Corporation.

Table of receiving-tube characteristics (RCA). Columns: Type | Name | Socket | Heater | Volts | Amps | Use | Plate Voltage | Grid Bias (volts) | Screen Voltage | Screen Current (ma) | Plate Current (ma) | Amplification Factor | Plate Resistance (ohms) | Transconductance (micromhos) | Load Resistance (ohms) | Power Output (watts)

Type	Name	Socket	Heater	Volts	Amps	Use	Plate V	Grid Bias	Screen V	Screen ma	Plate ma	Amp. Factor	Plate Res.	Transcond.	Load Res.	Power Output
6C6	Triple-Grid Detector Amplifier	D13	H	6.3	0.3	Amplifier Detector	For other characteristics, refer to Type 6J7.									
6C7	Duplex-Diode Triode	D9	H	6.3	0.3	Triode Unit as Class A Amplifier	250	– 9.0	—	—	4.5	20	16000	1250	—	—
6C8-G	Twin-Triode Amplifier	D8	H	6.3	0.3	Each Unit as Amplifier	250	– 4.5	—	—	3.2	36	22500	1600	—	—
6D6	Triple-Grid Supercontrol Amplifier	D13	H	6.3	0.3	Amplifier Mixer	For other characteristics, refer to Type 6U7-G.									
6D7	Triple-Grid Detector Amplifier	D13	H	6.3	0.3	Amplifier Detector	For other characteristics, refer to Type 6J7.									
6D8-G	Pentagrid Converter⊛	D8	H	6.3	0.15	Converter	135 / 250	– 3.0 / – 3.0	67.5 / 100	1.7 / 2.6	1.5 / 3.5		600000 / 400000			Anode-Grid (#2): 250 ℔ max. volts, 4.3 ma. Oscillator-Grid (#1) Resistor⊕. Conversion Transcond. 550 micromhos.
6E5	Electron-Ray Tube	D4	H	6.3	0.3	Visual Indicator	Plate & Target Supply = 125 volts. Triode Plate Resistor = 1.0 meg. Triode Plate Current = 0.8 ma. Grid Bias, –4.0 volts; Shadow Angle, 0°. Bias, 0 volts; Angle, 90°: Plate Current = 0.1 ma. / Plate & Target Supply = 250 volts. Triode Plate Resistor = 1.0 meg. Target Current = 2.0 ma. Grid Bias, –7.5 volts; Shadow Angle, 0°. Bias, 0 volts; Angle, 90°: Plate Current = 0.2 ma.									
6E6	Twin-Triode Power Amplifier	D12	H	6.3	0.6	Push-Pull Class A Amplifier	180 / 250	–20.0 / –27.5							15000 / 14000	0.75 / 1.60 — Power Output is for one tube at stated plate-to-plate load.
6E7	Triple-Grid Supercontrol Amplifier	D13	H	6.3	0.3	Amplifier	For other characteristics, refer to Type 6U7-G.									
6F5	High-Mu Triode	C1	H	6.3	0.3	Amplifier	For other characteristics, refer to Type 6SF5.									
6F5-GT	High-Mu Triode	C3	H	6.3	0.3	Amplifier	For other characteristics, refer to Type 6SF5.									
6F6	Power Pentodes	C2	H	6.3	0.7	Pentode Class A Amplifier	250 / 285	–16.5 / –20.0	250 / 285	6.5 / 7.0	34.0 / 38.0		80000 / 78000	2500 / 2550	7000 / 7000	3.2 / 4.8
						Triode□ Class A Amplifier	250	–20.0	—	—	31.0	6.8	2600	2600	4000	0.85
6F6-G	Power Pentodes	D10	H	6.3	0.7	Pentode Push-Pull Class A Amplifier	315 / 315	Cath. Bias –24.0	285 / 285	12.0⊕ / 12.0⊕	62.0⊕ / 62.0⊕		Cath. Bias Resistor, 320 ohms⊕		10000 / 10000	10.5† / 11.0†
6F6-GT	Power Pentodes	C5b	H	6.3	0.7	Pentode Push-Pull Class AB† Amplifier	375 / 375	Cath. Bias –26.0	250 / 250	8.0⊕ / 5.0⊕	54.0⊕ / 34.0⊕		Cath. Bias Resistor, 340 ohms⊕		10000 / 10000	19.0† / 18.5†
						Triode Push-Pull□ Class AB† Amplifier	350 / 350	Cath. Bias –38.0			50.0⊕ / 48.0⊕		Cath. Bias Resistor, 730 ohms⊕		10000 / 6000	9.0† / 13.0†
6F7	Triode-Pentode	D8	H	6.3	0.3	Triode Unit as Class A Amplifier	100	{ – 3.0 min. }	—	—	3.5	8	16000	500	—	—
						Pentode Unit as Class A Amplifier	100 / 250	{ – 3.0 min. }	100 / 100	1.6 / 1.5	6.3 / 6.3		290000 / 850000	1050 / 1100	—	—
						Pentode Unit as Mixer	250	–10.0	100	0.6	2.8		Oscillator Peak Volts = 7.0. Conversion Transcond. = 300 micromhos.			
6F8-G	Twin-Triode Amplifier	D8	H	6.3	0.6	Each Unit as Amplifier	For other characteristics, refer to Type 6J5.									

Reproduced with permission of RCA Corporation.

(RCA) Type	Name	Tube Dimensions	C.T.	Volts	Amp.	Use	Plate Supply Volts	Grid Bias Volts	Screen Supply Volts	Screen Current Ma	Plate Current Ma	AC Plate Resistance Ohms	Transconductance (Grid-plate) µmhos	Amplification Factor	Load for Stated Power Output Ohms	Power Output Watts	(RCA) Type
6G6-G	Power Amplifier Pentode	D8	H	6.3	0.15	Pentode Class A Amplifier	135 / 180	−6.0 / −9.0	135 / 180	2.0 / 2.5	11.5 / 15.0	170000 / 175000	2100 / 2300	—	12000 / 10000	0.6 / 1.1	6G6-G
						Triode] Class A Amplifier	180	−12.0			11.0	4750	2000	9.5	12000	0.25	
6H6, 6H6-GT	Twin Diodes	A1a / C3	H	6.3	0.3	Voltage Doubler	Max. A-C Supply Volts per Plate (RMS), 150 Total Effect. Plate-Supply Imped. per Plate: half-wave, 30 ohms; full-wave, 15 ohms.										6H6, 6H6-GT
						Half-Wave Rectifier	Max. A-C Plate Volts (RMS), 150 Max. D-C Output Ma., 8 per Plate. Min. Total Effective Plate-Supply Impedance: up to 117 volts, 15 ohms; at 150 volts, 40 ohms.										
6J5, 6J5-GT	Medium-Mu Triodes	B8 / C3	H	6.3	0.3	Class A Amplifier	90 / 250	0 / −8.0			10.0 / 9.0	6700 / 7700	3000 / 2600	20 / 20			6J5, 6J5-GT
6J6	Medium-Mu Twin Triode	B8	H	6.3	0.45	Each Unit as Class A Amplifier	100	Cathode Resistor, for both units, 50 ohms			8.5	7100	5300	38			6J6
						Push-Pull Class C Amplifier	150	−10.0	Cath. Res., 220 ohms, both units		30.0	Grid Current, 16 ma. Driving Power, 0.35 watt.				3.5	
6J7, 6J7-G, 6J7-GT	Sharp-Cutoff Pentodes	C1 / D8 / C3	H	6.3	0.3	Pentode Class A RF Amplifier	250	−3.0	100	0.5	2.0	1.0§	1185	Grid Resistor = 1.2 meg. ** Gain per stage = 85			6J7, 6J7-G, 6J7-GT
						Pentode Class A AF Amplifier	250	−3.0	100	0.5	2.0	1.0+§	1225	Grid Resistor = 1.2 meg. Gain per stage = 140			
						Pentode Bias Detector	250	−4.3	100	Cathode Current 0.43 ma.		Plate Resistor, 500000 ohms. Grid Resistor,** 250000 ohms.					
						Triode-⊥ Class A Amplifier	180 / 250	−5.3 / −8.0			5.3 / 6.5	11000 / 10500	1800 / 1900	20 / 20			
6J8-G	Triode-Heptode Converter	D8	H	6.3	0.3	Triode Unit as Oscillator	100 / 250	Triode-Grid Resistor, 50000 ohms				Triode-Grid & Heptode-Grid Current, 0.3 ma. / 0.4 ma.					6J8-G
						Heptode Unit as Mixer	100 / 250	−3.0 / −3.0	100 / 100	3.0 / 2.9	1.4 / 1.3	900000 / 4.0§	Conversion Transcond, 260 / 290 micromhos.				
6K5-GT	High-Mu Triode	D8	H	6.3	0.3	Class A Amplifier	100 / 250	−1.5 / −3.0			0.35 / 1.1	78000 / 50000	900 / 1400	70 / 70			6K5-GT
6K6-GT	Power Amplifier Pentode	C3	H	6.3	0.4	Single-Tube Class A Amplifier	100 / 250 / 315	−7.0 / −18.0 / −21.0	100 / 250 / 250	1.6 / 5.5 / 4.0	9.0 / 32.0 / 25.5	104000 / 68000 / 75000	1500 / 2300 / 2100		12000 / 7600 / 9000	0.35 / 3.40 / 4.50	6K6-GT
						Push-Pull Class A Amplifier	285 / 285	−25.5 Cath. Bias	285 / 285	9.0⊕ / 9.0⊕	55.0⊕ / 55.0⊕	Cath. Bias Resistor, 400 ohms⊕			12000 / 12000	10.5† / 9.8†	
6K7, 6K7-G, 6K7-GT	Remote-Cutoff Pentodes	C1 / D8 / C3	H	6.3	0.3	Class A Amplifier	100 / 250	−1.0 / −3.0	100 / 125	2.7 / 2.6	9.5 / 10.5	150000 / 600000	1650 / 1650				6K7, 6K7-G, 6K7-GT
6K8, 6K8-G, 6K8-GT	Triode-Hexode Converters	C1 / D8 / C7a	H	6.3	0.3	Triode Unit as Oscillator	100	Oscillator Peak Volts = 7.0			3.8	Triode-Grid & Hexode-Grid Current, 0.15 ma.					6K8, 6K8-G, 6K8-GT
						Hexode Unit as Mixer	100 / 250	−3.0 / −3.0	100 / 100	6.2 / 6.0	2.3 / 2.5	400000 / 600000	Conversion Transcond, 325 / 350 micromhos.	Triode-Grid Resistor, 50000 ohms			

This chart tabulates receiving-tube characteristics. Two values shown together in a cell (separated by " / ") represent two operating conditions as printed.

Type	Name	Socket	Heater	Htr V	Htr A	Use	Plate V	Screen (Grid-No.2) V	Grid-No.1 V	Screen mA	Plate mA	Plate Res. (ohms)	Transcond. (µmhos)	Amp. Factor	Load (ohms)	Power Output (watts)
6L5-G	Detector Amplifier Triode	D3	H	6.3	0.15	Single-Tube Class A Amplifier	135 / 250	—	−5.0 / −9.0	—	3.5 / 8.0	11300 / 9000	1500 / 1900	17 / 17	—	—
6L6	Beam Power Amplifiers	D7	H	6.3	0.9	Push-Pull Class A Amplifier	270 / 270	270 / 270	−17.5 / Cath. Bias (Cath. Bias Resistor, 170 ohms.)	11.0◆ / 11.0◆	134.0◆ / 134.0◆	—	—	—	5000 / 5000	17.5† / 18.5†
6L6	Beam Power Amplifiers	D7	H	6.3	0.9	Push-Pull AB₁ Amplifier	360 / 360	270 / 270	−22.5 / Cath. Bias (Cath. Bias Resistor, 125 ohms.)	5.0◆ / 5.0◆	88.0◆ / 88.0◆	—	—	—	6600 / 9000	26.5† / 24.5†
6L6-G	Beam Power Amplifiers	E2	H	6.3	0.9	Push-Pull Class AB₁ Amplifier	360 / 360	225 / 270	−18.0 / −22.5	3.5◆ / 5.0◆	78.0◆ / 88.0◆	—	—	—	6000 / 3800	31.0† / 47.0†
6L6-G	Beam Power Amplifiers	E2	H	6.3	0.9	Single Triode☐ Class A Amplifier	250 / 250	—	−20.0 / Cath. Bias (Cath. Bias Resistor, 490 ohms.)	—	40.0 / 40.0	1700 / 4700	—	8.0	5000 / 6000	1.4 / 1.3
6L7 / 6L7-G	Pentagrid Mixer▲	C1 / D8	H	6.3	0.3	Mixer in Superheterodyne	250	100	−3.0	—	2.4	—	—	—	—	—
6L7 / 6L7-G	Pentagrid Mixer▲	C1 / D8	H	6.3	0.3	Class A Amplifier	250	100	−3.0◆	—	5.3	—	1100	—	—	—

Oscillator-Grid (#3) Bias, −10 volts. Grid #3 Peak Swing, 12 volts. Conversion Transcond., 375 micromhos.

Type	Name	Socket	Heater	Htr V	Htr A	Use	Plate V	Screen V	Grid V	Screen mA	Plate mA	Plate Res.	Transcond.	Amp. Factor	Load	Power Output
6N6-G	Direct-Coupled Power Amplifier	D10	H	6.3	0.8	Class A Amplifier	—	—	—	—	—	—	—	—	Input	4.0

Output Triode: Plate Volts, 300; Plate Ma., 45; Load, 7000 ohms. Triode: Plate Volts, 300; Grid Volts, 0; A-F Signal Volts (Peak), 21; Plate Ma. 8.

Type	Name	Socket	Heater	Htr V	Htr A	Use	Plate V	Screen V	Grid V	Screen mA	Plate mA	Plate Res.	Transcond.	Amp. Factor	Load	Power Output
6N7	High-Mu Twin Power Triodes	C2 / C3	H	6.3	0.8	Class A Amplifier (as Driver)▽	250 / 294	—	−5.0 / −6.0	—	7.0 / 6.0	11300 / 11000	3100 / 3200	35 / 35	20000 or more	exceeds 0.4
6N7-GT	High-Mu Twin Power Triodes	C3	H	6.3	0.8	Class B Amplifier	300	—	0	—	—	—	—	—	8000	10.0

Power Output is for one tube at stated plate-to-plate load.

Type	Name	Socket	Heater	Htr V	Htr A	Use	Plate V	Screen V	Grid V	Screen mA	Plate mA	Plate Res.	Transcond.	Amp. Factor	Load	Power Output
6P5-GT	Detector Amplifier Triode	C3	H	6.3	0.3	Amplifier Detector	—	—	—	—	—	—	—	—	—	—

For other characteristics, refer to Type 76.

Type	Name	Socket	Heater	Htr V	Htr A	Use	Plate V	Screen V	Grid V	Screen mA	Plate mA	Plate Res.	Transcond.	Amp. Factor	Load	Power Output
6P7-G	Triode-Pentode	D8	H	6.3	0.3	Amplifier and Converter	—	—	—	—	—	—	—	—	—	—

For other characteristics, refer to Type 6F7.

Type	Name	Socket	Heater	Htr V	Htr A	Use	Plate V	Screen V	Grid V	Screen mA	Plate mA	Plate Res.	Transcond.	Amp. Factor	Load	Power Output
6Q7 / 6Q7-G / 6Q7-GT	Twin-Diode High-Mu Triodes	C1 / D8 / C3	H	6.3	0.3	Triode Unit as Class A Amplifier	100 / 250	—	−1.0 / −3.0 (Cath. Bias, 7600 ohms / Cath. Bias, 3000 ohms.)	—	0.8 / 1.1	58000 / 58000	1200 / 1200	70 / 70	Grid Resistor, 0.5 megohm.	—
6R7 / 6R7-G / 6R7-GT	Twin-Diode Medium-Mu Triodes	C1 / D8 / C3	H	6.3	0.3	Triode Unit as Class A Amplifier	90▼ / 300▼	—	−9.0 (Cath. Bias, 4400 ohms / Cath. Bias, 3800 ohms.)	—	9.5	8500	1900	16	Grid Resistor, 0.25 megohm.	—
6S7 / 6S7-G	Remote-Cutoff Pentodes	C1 / D8	H	6.3	0.3	Class A Amplifier	135 / 250	67.5 / 100	−3.0 / −3.0	0.9 / 2.0	3.7 / 8.5	1.0§ / 1.0§	1250 / 1750	—	—	—
6S8-GT	Triple-Diode Triode	C7b	H	6.3	0.3	Triode Unit as Class A Amplifier	100 / 250	—	−1.0 / −2.0	—	0.4 / 0.9	110000 / 91000	900 / 1100	100 / 100	—	—
6SA7	Pentagrid Converter▲	B3	H	6.3	0.3	Mixer	100 / 250	100 / 100	Self-Excited	—	3.3 / 3.5	500000 / 1.0§	—	—	—	8.5 / 8.5

Grid #1 Resistor, 20000 ohms. Conversion Transcond. .450 micromhos.

Type	Name	Socket	Heater	Htr V	Htr A	Use	Plate V	Screen V	Grid V	Screen mA	Plate mA	Plate Res.	Transcond.	Amp. Factor	Load	Power Output
6SA7-GT	Pentagrid Converter▲	C3	H	6.3	0.3	Mixer	—	—	—	—	—	—	—	—	—	—

For other characteristics, refer to Type 6SA7.

Type	Name	Socket	Heater	Htr V	Htr A	Use	Plate V	Screen V	Grid V	Screen mA	Plate mA	Plate Res.	Transcond.	Amp. Factor	Load	Power Output
6SB7-Y	Pentagrid Converter▲	B3	H	6.3	0.3	Mixer	100 / 250	100 / 100	−1.0 / −1.0	—	3.6 / 3.8	500000 / 1.0§	—	—	—	10.2 / 10.0

Grid #1 Resistor, 20000 ohms. Conversion Transcond. .950 micromhos.

RCA Type	Name	Tube Dimensions	Cathode Type and Rating			Use	Plate Supply Volts	Grid Bias Volts	Screen Supply Volts	Screen Current Ma.	Plate Current Ma.	AC Plate Resistance Ohms	Transconductance (Grid-plate) µmhos	Amplification Factor	Load for Stated Power Output Ohms	Power Output Watts	RCA Type
			C.T.	Volts	Amp.	Values to right give operating conditions and characteristics for indicated typical uses											
6SC7	Twin-Triode Amplifier	B3	H	6.3	0.3	Each Unit as Amplifier	250	-2.0	—	—	2.0	53000	1325	70	—	—	6SC7
6SF5	High-Mu Triodes	B3	H	6.3	0.3	Class A Amplifier	100 / 250	-1.0 / -2.0	—	—	0.4 / 0.9	85000 / 66000	1150 / 1500	100 / 100	—	—	6SF5
6SF5-GT		C3					90M / 300M	Cath. Bias, 8800 ohms, 3200 ohms							Gain per stage = 43 / Gain per stage = 63		6SF5-GT
						Grid Resistor,** 0.5 megohm.											
6SF7	Diode-Remote-Cutoff Pentode	B3	H	6.3	0.3	Pentode Unit as Class A Amplifier	100 / 250	-1.0 / -1.0	100 / 100	4.3 / 4.1	13.5 / 13.9	200000 / 700000	1975 / 2050	—	—	—	6SF7
6SG7	Semi-Remote-Cutoff Pentode	B3	H	6.3	0.3	Class A Amplifier	100 / 250 / 250	-1.0 / -1.0 / -2.5	100 / 125 / 150	3.2 / 4.4 / 3.4	8.2 / 11.8 / 9.2	250000 / 900000 / 1.0+§	4100 / 4700 / 4000	—	—	—	6SG7
6SH7	Sharp-Cutoff Pentode	B3	H	6.3	0.3	Class A Amplifier	100 / 250	-.0 / -1.0	100 / 150	2.1 / 4.1	5.3 / 10.8	350000 / 900000	4000 / 4900	—	—	—	6SH7
6SJ7	Sharp-Cutoff Pentodes	B3	H	6.3	0.3	Class A Amplifier	100 / 250	-3.0 / -3.0	100 / 100	0.9 / 0.8	2.9 / 3.0	700000 / 1.0+§	1575 / 1650	—	—	—	6SJ7
6SJ7-GT		C3					90M / 300M	Cath. Bias, 1700 ohms, 860 ohms							Gain per stage = 93 / Gain per stage = 167		6SJ7-GT
						Grid Resistor,** 0.5 megohm.											
6SK7	Remote-Cutoff Pentodes	B3	H	6.3	0.3	Class A Amplifier	100 / 250	-1.0 / -3.0	100 / 100	4.0 / 2.6	13.0 / 9.2	120000 / 800000	2350 / 2000	—	—	—	6SK7
6SK7-GT		C3															6SK7-GT
						Grid Resistor,** 0.5 megohm.											
6SL7-GT	Twin-Triode Amplifier	C3	H	6.3	0.3	Each Unit as Amplifier	250	-2.0	—	—	2.3	44000	1600	70	—	—	6SL7-GT
6SN7-GT	Twin-Triode Amplifier	C3	H	6.3	0.6	Each Unit as Amplifier					For other characteristics, refer to Type 6J5.						6SN7-GT
6SQ7	Twin-Diode High-Mu Triodes	B3	H	6.3	0.3	Triode Unit as Class A Amplifier	100 / 250	-1.0 / -2.0	—	—	0.4 / 0.9	110000 / 91000	900 / 1100	100 / 100	—	—	6SQ7
6SQ7-GT		C3					90M / 300M	Cath. Bias, 11000 ohms, 3900 ohms							Gain per stage = 40 / Gain per stage = 53		6SQ7-GT
						Grid Resistor, ** 0.5 megohm.											
6SR7	Duplex-Diode Triode	B3	H	6.3	0.3	Triode Unit as Class A Amplifier	250	-9.0	—	—	9.5	8500	1900	16	10000	0.3	6SR7
6SS7	Triple-Grid Supercontrol Amplifier	B3	H	6.3	0.15	Class A Amplifier	100 / 250	-1.0 / -3.0	100 / 100	3.1 / 2.0	12.2 / 9.0	120000 / 1.0§	1930 / 1850	—	—	—	6SS7
6ST7	Duplex-Diode Triode	B3	H	6.3	0.15	Triode Unit as Amplifier					For other characteristics, refer to Type 6SR7.						6ST7
6SZ7	Duplex-Diode High-Mu Triode	B3	H	6.3	0.15	Triode Unit as Class A Amplifier	100 / 250	-1.0 / -3.0	—	—	0.8 / 1.0	61000 / 58000	1150 / 1200	70 / 70	—	—	6SZ7
6T7-G	Duplex-Diode High-Mu Triode	D6	H	6.3	0.15	Triode Unit as Class A Amplifier	135 / 250 / 90M / 300M	-1.5 / -3.0 / Cath. Bias, 8300 ohms, 4580 ohms	—	—	0.9 / 1.2	65000 / 62000	1000 / 1050	65 / 65		Gain per stage = 30 / Gain per stage = 40	6T7-G
						Grid Resistor,** 0.5 megohm.											

Plate & Target Supply = 250 volts. Triode Plate Resistor = 1.0 meg. Target Current = 4.0 ma. Grid Bias, −22 volts; Shadow Angle, 0°. Plate, 90°, 0 volts: Plate Current, 0.24 ma.

Type	Tube	Base	Cath.	Heater Volts	Heater Amps	Use	Plate Volts	Grid Volts	Screen Volts	Screen Ma.	Plate Ma.	Plate Res. (Ohms)	Transcond. (μmhos)	Load Res. (Ohms)	Power Output (Watts)
6U7-G	Triple-Grid Supercontrol Amplifier	D12a	H	6.3	0.3	Class A Amplifier	100 / 250	−3.0 / −3.0	100 / 100	2.2 / 2.0	8.0 / 8.2	250000 / 800000	1500 / 1600		
						Mixer in Superheterodyne	100 / 250	−10.0 / −10.0	100 / 100					Oscillator Peak Volts = 7.0	
6V6	Beam Power Amplifiers	C2	H	6.3	0.45	Single-Tube Class A Amplifier	180 / 250 / 315	−8.5 / −12.5 / −13.0	180 / 250 / 225	3.0 / 4.5 / 2.2	29.0 / 45.0 / 34.0	58000 / 52000 / 77000	3700 / 4100 / 3750	5500 / 5000 / 8500	2.0 / 4.5 / 5.5
6V6-GT		C3				Push-Pull Class AB₂ Amplifier	250 / 285	−15.0 / −19.0	250 / 285	5.0◆ / 4.0◆	70.0◆ / 70.0◆			10000 / 8000	10.0† / 14.0†
6V7-G	Duplex-Diode Triode	D8	H	6.3	0.3	Triode Unit as Amplifier	For other characteristics, refer to Type 85.								
6W7-G	Triple-Grid Detector Amplifier	D8	H	6.3	0.15	Class A Amplifier	250	−3.0	100	0.5	2.0	1.5§	1225		
6X4	Full-Wave Rectifier	B1a	H	6.3	0.6	With Capacitive-Input Filter	Max. A-C Volts per Plate (RMS), 325	Max. Peak Inverse Volts, 1250	Max. D-C Output Ma. 70	Max. Peak Plate Ma. 210				Min. Total Effect. Supply Imped. per Plate, 150 ohm	
						With Inductive-Input Filter	Max. A-C Volts per Plate (RMS), 450	Max. Peak Inverse Volts, 1250	Max. D-C Output Ma. 70	Max. Peak Plate Ma. 210				Min. Value of Input Choke, 8 henries	
6X5	Full-Wave Rectifiers	C2	H	6.3	0.6	With Capacitive-Input Filter	Max. A-C Volts per Plate (RMS), 325	Max. Peak Inverse Volts, 1250	Max. D-C Output Ma. 70	Max. Peak Plate Ma. 210				Min. Total Effect. Supply Imped. per Plate, 150 ohm	
6X5-GT		C3				With Inductive-Input Filter	Max. A-C Volts per Plate (RMS), 450	Max. Peak Inverse Volts, 1250	Max. D-C Output Ma. 70	Max. Peak Plate Ma. 210				Min. Value of Input Choke, 8 henries	
6Y5	Full-Wave Rectifier	D5	H	6.3	0.8	With Capacitive-Input Filter	135						Max. A-C Volts per Plate (RMS), 350 — Max. D-C Output Ma. 50		
						With Inductive-Input Filter	200								
6Y6-G	Beam Power Amplifier	D10	H	6.3	1.25	Single-Tube Class A Amplifier	135 / 135	−13.5 / −14.0	135 / 135	3.5 / 2.2	58.0 / 61.0	9300 / 18300	7000 / 7100	2000 / 2600	3.6 / 6.0
6Y7-G	Twin-Triode Amplifier	D3	H	6.3	0.6	Class B Amplifier	For other characteristics, refer to Type 79.								
6Z5	Full-Wave Rectifier	D5	H	6.3 / 12.6	0.8 / 0.4	With Capacitive-Input Filter	Max. A-C Volts per Plate (RMS), 230	Max. D-C Output Ma. 60							
6Z7-G	Twin-Triode Amplifier	D3	H	6.3	0.3	Class B Amplifier	135 / 180	0 / 0					9000 / 12000		2.5 / 4.2
						Power Output is for one tube at stated plate-to-plate load.									
6ZY5-G	Full-Wave Rectifier	D3	H	6.3	0.3	With Capacitive-Input Filter	Max. A-C Volts per Plate (RMS), 325	Max. Peak Inverse Volts, 1250	Max. D-C Output Ma. 40	Max. Peak Plate Ma. 120				Min. Total Effect. Supply Imped. per Plate, 225 ohm	
						With Inductive-Input Filter	Max. A-C Volts per Plate (RMS), 450	Max. Peak Inverse Volts, 1250	Max. D-C Output Ma. 40	Max. Peak Plate Ma. 140				Min. Value of Input Choke, 13.5 henries	
7A4	Detector Amplifier Triode	B5	H	6.3	0.3	Amplifier	For other characteristics, refer to Type 6J5.								
7A5	Beam Power Amplifier	C4	H	6.3	0.75	Class A Amplifier	110 / 125	−7.5 / −9.0	110 / 125	3.0 / 3.3	40.0 / 44.0	14000 / 17000	5800 / 6000	2500 / 2700	1.5 / 2.2
7A6	Twin Diode	B5	H	6.3	0.15	Detector Rectifier	Maximum A-C Voltage per Plate .... 150 Volts, RMS — Maximum D-C Output Current per plate .... 8 Milliamperes								
7A7	Triple-Grid Supercontrol Amplifier	B8	H	6.3	0.3	Class A Amplifier	For other characteristics, refer to Type 6SK7.								

Reproduced with permission of RCA Corporation.

RCA Type	Name	Tube Dimensions	Cathode C.T.	Cathode Volts	Cathode Amp.	Use	Plate Supply Volts	Grid Bias Volts	Screen Supply Volts	Screen Current Ma	Plate Current Ma	AC Plate Resistance Ohms	Transconductance (Grid-plate) µmhos	Amplification Factor	Load for Stated Power Output Ohms	Power Output Watts	RCA Type
7A8	Octode Converter	B5	H	6.3	0.15	Converter	100 / 250	− 3.0 / − 3.0	75 / 100	2.7 / 3.2	1.8 / 3.0	650000 / 700000		Anode-Grid (#2): 250 b max. volts. Anode-Grid (#1) Resistor e. 4.2 ma. Oscillator-Grid (#1) Resistor e. Conversion Transcond., 550 micromhos.			7A8
7B4	High-Mu Triode	B5	H	6.3	0.3	Amplifier	For other characteristics, refer to Type 6SF5.										7B4
7B5	Power Amplifier Pentode	C8	H	6.3	0.4	Class A Amplifier	For other characteristics, refer to Type 6K6-GT.										7B5
7B6	Duplex-Diode High-Mu Triode	B8	H	6.3	0.3	Triode Unit as Amplifier	For other characteristics, refer to Type 6SQ7.										7B6
7B7	Triple-Grid Supercontrol Amplifier	B8	H	6.3	0.15	Class A Amplifier	250	− 3.0	100	1.7	8.5	750000	1750	—	—	—	7B7
7B8	Pentagrid Converter	B8	H	6.3	0.3	Converter	For other characteristics, refer to Type 6A8.										7B8
7C5	Beam Power Amplifier	C8	H	6.3	0.45	Class A Amplifier	For other characteristics, refer to Type 6V6-GT.										7C5
7C6	Duplex-Diode High-Mu Triode	B8	H	6.3	0.15	Triode Unit as Class A Amplifier	250	− 1.0	—	—	1.3	100000	1000	100	—	—	7C6
7C7	Triple-Grid Detector Amplifier	B8	H	6.3	0.15	Class A Amplifier	100 / 250	− 3.0 / − 3.0	100 / 100	0.4 / 0.5	1.8 / 2.0	1.2§ / 2.0§	1225 / 1300	—	—	—	7C7
7DP4	Directly Viewed Kinescope	11	H	6.3	0.6	Picture Reproduction	Focus: Electrostatic Deflection: Magnetic Deflection Angle: 50° Phosphor: No. 4 Picture Size: 4" x 5½" Uses Ion-Trap Magnet			Anode-No. 2 Volts, 8000 (for Focus, Anode-No. 1 Volts for Focus, 1216 to 1644 (2400 max.), Grid-No. 2 Volts, 250 (410 max.) Grid-No. 1 Volts for Visual Cutoff, −27 to −63				Anode-No. 1 Current Range, −15 to +10 microamperes Ion-Trap Magnet Current, 70 approx. ma. (dc) Deflection Coil Current, 410 approx. ma. (dc)			7DP4
7E6	Duplex-Diode Triode	B5	H	6.3	0.3	Triode Unit as Amplifier	For other characteristics, refer to Type 6R7.										7E6
7E7	Duplex-Diode Pentode	B8	H	6.3	0.3	Pentode Unit as Class A Amplifier	100 / 250	− 1.0 / − 3.0	100 / 100	2.7 / 1.6	10.0 / 7.5	150000 / 700000	1600 / 1300	—	—	—	7E7
7F7	Twin-Triode Amplifier	B8	H	6.3	0.3	Each Unit as Amplifier	For other characteristics, refer to Type 6SL7-GT.										7F7
7F8	Twin-Triode Amplifier	B0b	H	6.3	0.3	Each Unit as Class A Amplifier	250	Cathode-Bias Res., 500 ohms	—	—	6.0	—	3300	48	—	—	7F8
7G7/1232	Television Amplifier Pentode	B5	H	6.3	0.45	Class A Amplifier	250	− 2.0	100	2.0	6.0	800000	4500	—	—	—	7G7/1232
7GP4	Directly Viewed Kinescope	11a	H	6.3	0.6	Picture Reproduction	Anode-No. 2 and Grid-No. 2 Volts, 4000 (max.). Anode-No. 1 Volts for Focus, 1080 to 1600 Grid-No. 1 Volts for Visual Cutoff, 48 to 112						For other characteristics, refer to Type 7JP4.				7GP4

Type	Description	Base	F/H	Heater V	Heater A	Use	Plate V	Grid V	Screen V	Screen mA	Plate mA	Plate Res. (Ω)	Transcond. (μmho)	Amp. Factor	Notes
7H7	Triple-Grid Supercontrol Amplifier	B5	H	6.3	0.3	Class A Amplifier	100/250	−1.0/−2.5	100/100	3.3/3.5	8.2/9.5	250000/800000	3800/3800	—	—
7J7	Triode-Heptode Converter	B8	H	6.3	0.3	Triode Unit as Oscillator / Heptode Unit as Mixer	100/250	−3.0/−3.0	100/100	2.6/2.8	1.5/1.4	500000/1.5§	—	—	Triode Unit as Oscillator: Triode-Grid Resistor, 50000 ohms. Triode-Grid & Heptode-Grid Current, 0.3 ma. / 0.4 ma. Conversion Transcond., 280 / 290 micromhos.
7JP4	Directly Viewed Kinescope	11a	H	6.3	0.6	Picture Reproduction									Focus: Electrostatic; Deflection: Electrostatic; Phosphor: No. 4; Picture Size: 4" x 5½". Anode-No. 2 and Grid-No. 2 Volts, 6000 (max.). Anode-No. 1 Current Range, 1620 to 2400 (2500 max.). Grid-No. 1 Volts for Visual Cutoff, −15 to + 10 microamperes. Deflection Factors: DJ₁ and DJ₃ (nearer base), −72 to −168; 31 to 41 vdc/in./kv; DJ₂ and DJ₄ (nearer screen), 25 to 34 vdc/in./kv.
7L7	RF Amplifier Pentode	B5	H	6.3	0.3	Class A Amplifier	100/250	−1.0/−1.5	100/100	2.4/1.5	5.5/4.5	100000/1.0§	3000/3100	—	—
7N7	Twin-Triode Amplifier	C6	H	6.3	0.6	Each Unit as Class A Amplifier									For other characteristics, refer to Type 6SN7-GT.
7Q7	Pentagrid Converter ▲	B5	H	6.3	0.3	Converter	100/250	−2.0/−2.0	100/100	8.5/8.5	3.3/3.5	500000/1.0§	550	—	Grid #1 Resistor, 20000 ohms. Conversion Transcond., 550 micromhos.
7R7	Duplex-Diode Pentode	B5	H	6.3	0.3	Pentode Unit as Class A Amplifier	100/250	−1.0/−1.0	100/100	2.2/1.6	5.5/6.2	350000/1.0§	3000/3400	—	—
7S7	Triode-Heptode Converter	B5	H	6.3	0.3	Triode Unit as Oscillator / Heptode Unit as Mixer	100/250	−2.0/−2.0	100/100	3.0/3.0	1.9/1.8	500000/1.25§	500/525	—	Triode Unit as Oscillator: Triode-Grid Resistor, 50000 ohms. Triode-Grid & Heptode-Grid Current, 0.3 ma. / 0.4 ma. Conversion Transcond., 500 / 525 micromhos.
7V7	RF Amplifier Pentode	B5	H	6.3	0.45	Class A Amplifier	300	150		3.9	10.0	300000	5800	—	Cath. Bias Res., 160 ohms.
7W7	RF Amplifier Pentode	B5	H	6.3	0.45	Class A Amplifier									For other characteristics, refer to Type 7V7.
7Y4	Full-Wave Rectifier	B5	H	6.3	0.5	With Capacitive-Input Filter / With Inductive-Input Filter									Max. A-C Volts per Plate (RMS), 325 / 450. Max. Peak Inverse Volts, 1250 / 1250. Max. D-C Output Ma., 70 / 70. Max. Peak Plate Ma., 180 / 180. Min. Total Effec. Supply Imped. per Plate, 150 ohms. Min. Value of Input Choke, 10 henries.
7Z4	Full-Wave Rectifier	C8	H	6.3	0.9	With Capacitive-Input Filter / With Inductive-Input Filter									Max. A-C Volts per Plate (RMS), 325 / 450. Max. Peak Inverse Volts, 1250 / 1250. Max. D-C Output Ma., 100 / 100. Max. Peak Plate Ma., 300 / 300. Min. Total Effec. Supply Imped. per Plate, 75 ohms. Min. Value of Input Choke, 6 henries.
9AP4	Directly Viewed Kinescope	K7	H	2.5	2.1	Picture Reproduction									Focus: Electrostatic; Deflection: Magnetic; Phosphor: No. 4; Picture Size: 5¾" x 7¼". Anode Volts, 7000 (max.). Anode-No. 1 Volts for Focus, 1192 to 1788 (2000 max.). Grid-No. 2 Volts, 250 (300 max.). Grid-No. 1 Volts for Visual Cutoff, −20 to −60. Grid-No. 1 Signal Voltage, (Peak-to-Peak) value, 30 volts approx.
10	Power Amplifier Triode	E3	F	7.5	1.25	Class A Amplifier	350/425	−31/−39			16.0/18.0	5150/5000	1550/1600	8.0/8.0	Load 11000/10200 ohms; Power Output 0.9/1.6.
10BP4	Directly Viewed Kinescope	J1	H	6.3	0.6	Picture Reproduction									Focus: Magnetic; Deflection: Magnetic; Deflection Angle: 50°; Phosphor: No. 4; Picture Size: 6" x 8". Uses Ion-Trap Magnet. Anode Volts, 10000. Grid-No. 2 Volts, 250 (450 max.). Grid-No. 1 Volts for Visual Cutoff, −27 to −63. Grid-No. 1 Circuit Resistance, 1.5 megohms (max.). Focusing Coil Circuit, 115 approx. ma. (dc). Ion-Trap Magnet Current, 109 approx. ma. (dc). Deflection Coil Current, 470 approx. ma. (dc).

Reproduced with permission of RCA Corporation.

Type	Name	Tube Dimensions	Cathode Type and Rating C.T.	Volts	Amp.	Use	Plate Supply Volts	Grid Bias Volts	Screen Supply Volts	Screen Current Ma	Plate Current Ma	AC Plate Resistance Ohms	Transconductance (Grid-plate) μmhos	Amplification Factor	Load for Stated Power Output Ohms	Power Output Watts	Type
11 12	Detector★ Amplifier Triodes	D2 D11	D.C. F	1.1	0.25	Class A Amplifier	90 135	−4.5 −10.5	— —	—	2.5 3.0	15500 15000	425 440	6.6 6.6	— —	— —	11 12
12A5	Power Amplifier Pentode	D5	H	6.3 12.6	0.6 0.3	Class A Amplifier	100 180	−15.0 −25.0	100 180	3.0 8.0	17.0 45.0	50000 35000	1700 2400	—	4500 3300	0.8 3.4	12A5
12A7	Rectifier-Pentode	D9	H	12.6	0.3	Pentode Unit as Class A Amplifier	135	−13.5	135	2.5	9.0	102000	975	—	13500	0.55	12A7
						Half-Wave Rectifier	Maximum A-C Plate Voltage...........125 Volts, RMS Maximum D-C Output Current..........30 Milliamperes										
12A8-GT	Pentagrid Converter ⊙	C3	H	12.6	0.15	Converter	For other characteristics, refer to Type 6A8.										12A8-GT
12AH7-GT	Twin Triode	C9	H	12.6	0.15	Each Unit as Class A Amplifier	100 180	−3.6 −6.5	—	—	3.7 7.6	10300 8400	1550 1900	16 16	—	—	12AH7-GT
12AL5	Twin-Diode	A1	H	12.6	0.15	Detector Rectifier	For other characteristics, refer to Type 6AL5.										12AL5
12AP4	Directly Viewed Kinescope	L1	H	2.5	2.1	Picture Reproduction	Focus: Electrostatic Deflection: Magnetic Phosphor: No. 4 Picture Size: 7⅞" x 9¾"	Anode-No. 2 Volts, 7000 (max.) Anode-No. 1 Volts for Focus, 1192 to 1788 (2000 max.)	Grid-No. 1 Volts for Visual Cutoff, −20 to −60 Grid-No. 1 Signal Voltage, (Peak-to-Peak) value, 30 volts approx. Grid-No. 2 Volts 250 (300 max.)								12AP4
12AT6	Duplex-Diode High-Mu Triode	B0	H	12.6	0.15	Triode Unit as Class A Amplifier	For other characteristics, refer to Type 6AT6.										12AT6
12AU6	RF Amplifier Pentode	B0	H	12.6	0.15	Class A Amplifier	For other characteristics, refer to Type 6AU6.										12AU6
12AU7	Twin-Triode Amplifier	B0a	H	6.3 12.6	0.3 0.15	Each Unit As Class A Amplifier	100 250	0 −8.5	—	—	11.8 10.5	6250 7700	3100 2200	19.5 17	—	—	12AU7
12AV6	Twin-Diode High-Mu Triode	B0	H	12.6	0.15	Triode Unit as Class A Amplifier	For other characteristics, refer to Type 6AV6.										12AV6
12AW6	RF Amplifier Pentode	B0	H	12.6	0.15	Class A Amplifier	For other characteristics, refer to Type 6AG5.										12AW6
12AX7	High-Mu Twin Triode	B0a	H	6.3 12.6	0.3 0.15	As Triode ☐ Each Unit as Class A Amplifier	100 250	−1.0 −2.0	—	—	0.5 1.2	80000 62500	1250 1600	100 100	—	—	12AX7
12B8-GT	Triode-Pentode	C7a	H	12.6	0.3	Triode Unit as Class A Amplifier	90	0	—	—	2.8	37000	2400	90	—	—	12B8-GT
						Pentode Unit as Class A Amplifier	90	−3.0	90	2.0	7.0	200000	1800	—	—	—	
12BA6	RF Amplifier Pentode	B0	H	12.6	0.15	Class A Amplifier	For other characteristics, refer to Type 6BA6.										12BA6
12BE6	Pentagrid Converter ▲	B0	H	12.6	0.15	Converter	For other characteristics, refer to Type 6BE6.										12BE6

Type	Pentode		H	12.6		Pentode Unit as AF Amplifier	90 Cath. Bias, 3500 ohms. Screen Resistor = 1.1 meg / 300 Cath. Bias, 1600 ohms. Screen Resistor = 1.2 meg — Grid Resistor 0.5 megohm. — Gain per stage = 55 / Gain per stage = 79	Type
12F5-GT	High-Mu Triode	C3	H	12.6	0.15	Amplifier	For other characteristics, refer to Type 6SJ5.	12F5-GT
12H6	Twin-Diode	A1	H	12.6	0.15	Detector Rectifier	For other ratings, refer to Type 6H6.	12H6
12J5-GT	Detector Amplifier Triode	C3	H	12.6	0.15	Amplifier	For other characteristics, refer to Type 6J5.	12J5-GT
12J7-GT	Triple-Grid Detector Amplifier	C3	H	12.6	0.15	Amplifier	For other characteristics, refer to Type 6J7.	12J7-GT
12K7-GT	Triple-Grid Supercontrol Amplifier	C3	H	12.6	0.15	Amplifier	For other characteristics, refer to Type 6K7.	12K7-GT
12K8	Triode-Hexode Converter	C1	H	12.6	0.15	Oscillator Mixer	For other characteristics, refer to Type 6K8.	12K8
12Q7-GT	Duplex-Diode High-Mu Triode	C3	H	12.6	0.15	Triode Unit as Amplifier	For other characteristics, refer to Type 6Q7.	12Q7-GT
12SA7	Pentagrid Converter▲	B3	H	12.6	0.15	Mixer	For other characteristics, refer to Type 6SA7.	12SA7
12SA7-GT	Pentagrid Converter▲	C3	H	12.6	0.15	Mixer	For other characteristics, refer to Type 6SA7.	12SA7-GT
12SC7	Twin-Triode Amplifier	B3	H	12.6	0.15	Each Unit as Class A Amplifier	For other characteristics, refer to Type 6SC7.	12SC7
12SF5	High-Mu Triode	B3	H	12.6	0.15	Class A Amplifier	For other characteristics, refer to Type 6SF5.	12SF5
12SF5-GT	High-Mu Triode	C3	H	12.6	0.15	Class A Amplifier	For other characteristics, refer to Type 6SF5.	12SF5-GT
12SF7	Diode-Remote-Cutoff Pentode	B3	H	12.6	0.15	Pentode Unit as Amplifier	For other characteristics, refer to Type 6SF7.	12SF7
12SG7	Semi-Remote-Cutoff Pentode	B3	H	12.6	0.15	Class A Amplifier	For other characteristics, refer to Type 6SG7.	12SG7
12SH7	Sharp-Cutoff Pentode	B3	H	12.6	0.15	Class A Amplifier	For other characteristics, refer to Type 6SH7.	12SH7
12SJ7 / 12SJ7-GT	Sharp-Cutoff Pentodes	B3 / C3	H	12.6	0.15	Class A Amplifier	For other characteristics, refer to Type 6SJ7.	12SJ7 / 12SJ7-GT
12SK7 / 12SK7-GT	Remote-Cutoff Pentodes	B3 / C3	H	12.6	0.15	Class A Amplifier	For other characteristics, refer to Type 6SK7.	12SK7 / 12SK7-GT
12SL7-GT	Twin-Triode Amplifier	C3	H	12.6	0.15	Each Unit as Amplifier	For other characteristics, refer to Type 6SL7-GT.	12SL7-GT
12SN7-GT	Twin-Triode Amplifier	C3	H	12.6	0.3	Each Unit as Amplifier	For other characteristics, refer to Type 6J5.	12SN7-GT
12SQ7	Duplex-Diode High-Mu Triode	B3	H	12.6	0.15	Triode Unit as Amplifier	For other characteristics, refer to Type 6SQ7.	12SQ7

RCA Type	Name	Tube Dimensions	Cathode Type and Rating C.T.	Volts	Amp.	Use — Values to right give operating conditions and characteristics for indicated typical use	Plate Supply Volts	Grid Bias Volts	Screen Supply Volts	Screen Current Ma.	Plate Current Ma.	AC Plate Resistance Ohms	Transconductance (Grid-plate) μmhos	Amplification Factor	Load for Stated Power Output Ohms	Power Output Watts	RCA Type
12SQ7-GT	Duplex-Diode High-Mu Triode	C3	H	12.6	0.15	Triode Unit as Amplifier						For other characteristics, refer to Type 6SQ7.					12SQ7-GT
12SR7	Duplex-Diode Triode	B3	H	12.6	0.15	Triode Unit as Amplifier						For other characteristics, refer to Type 6SR7.					12SR7
12SR7-GT	Duplex-Diode Triode	C3	H	12.6	0.15	Triode Unit as Amplifier						For other characteristics, refer to Type 6SR7.					12SR7-GT
12Z3	Half-Wave Rectifier	D5	H	12.6	0.3	With Capacitive-Input Filter						Max. A-C Plate Volts (RMS), 235 — Min. Total Effective Plate-Supply Impedance: Up to 117 volts, 0 ohms; at 150 volts, 30 ohms; at 235 volts, 75 ohms. Max. D-C Output Ma., 55					12Z3
14A4	Detector Amplifier Triode	B5	H	12.6	0.15	Class A Amplifier						For other characteristics, refer to Type 6J5.					14A4
14A5	Beam Power Amplifier	B5	H	12.6	0.15	Class A Amplifier	250	−12.5	250	3.5	30	70000	3000	—	7500	2.8	14A5
14A7/12B7	Triple-Grid Supercontrol Amplifier	B5	H	12.6	0.15	Class A Amplifier	100 / 250	− 1.0 / − 3.0	100 / 100	4.0 / 2.6	13.0 / 9.2	120000 / 800000	2350 / 2000	—	—	—	14A7/12B7
14B6	Duplex-Diode High-Mu Triode	B5	H	12.6	0.15	Triode Unit as Class A Amplifier						For other characteristics, refer to Type 6SQ7.					14B6
14B8	Pentagrid Converter	B5	H	12.6	0.15	Converter						For other characteristics, refer to Type 6A8.					14B8
14C7	Triple-Grid Detector Amplifier	B5	H	12.6	0.15	Class A Amplifier						For other characteristics, refer to Type 6SJ7.					14C7
14E6	Duplex-Diode Triode	B5	H	12.6	0.15	Triode Unit as Class A Amplifier						For other characteristics, refer to Type 6SR7.					14E6
14F7	Twin-Triode Amplifier	B5	H	12.6	0.15	Each Unit as Class A Amplifier						For other characteristics, refer to Type 6SL7-GT.					14F7
14H7	Triple-Grid Supercontrol Amplifier	B5	H	12.6	0.15	Class A Amplifier						For other characteristics, refer to Type 7H7.					14H7
14J7	Triode-Heptode Converter	B5	H	12.6	0.15	Converter						For other characteristics, refer to Type 7J7.					14J7
14N7	Twin-Triode Amplifier	C6	H	12.6	0.3	Each Unit as Class A Amplifier						For other characteristics, refer to Type 6SN7-GT.					14N7
14Q7	Pentagrid Converter	B5	H	12.6	0.15	Converter						For other characteristics, refer to Type 6SA7.					14Q7
14R7	Duplex-Diode Pentode	B5	H	12.6	0.15	Pentode Unit as Class A Amplifier						For other characteristics, refer to Type 7R7.					14R7
15	RF Amplifier Pentode	D9	D.C. H	2.0	0.22	Class A Amplifier	67.5 / 135	− 1.5 / − 1.5	67.5 / 67.5	0.3 / 0.3	1.85 / 1.85	630000 / 800000	710 / 750	—	—	—	15

Type		Base	Fil. or Heater	Volts	Amp.	Class of Service	Plate Volts	Grid Volts	Screen Volts	Screen Ma.	Plate Ma.	Plate Resistance (ohms)	Transconductance (µmhos)	Amplification Factor	Load (ohms)	Power Output (watts)	Type
20	Power Amplifier Triode	D1	D.C. F	3.3	0.132	Class A Amplifier	90 / 135	−16.5 / −22.5	—	—	3.0 / 6.5	8000 / 6300	415 / 525	3.3 / 3.3	9600 / 6500	0.045 / 0.110	20
22	RF Amplifier Tetrode	E1	D.C. F	3.3	0.132	Screen-Grid RF Amplifier	135 / 135	−1.5 / −1.5	45 / 61.5	0.6* / 1.3*	1.7 / 3.7	125000 / 335000	375 / 500	—	—	—	22
24-A	RF Amplifier Tetrode	E1	H	2.5	1.75	Screen-Grid RF Amplifier	180 / 250	−3.0 / −3.0	90 / 90	1.7* / 1.7*	4.0 / 4.0	400000 / 600000	1000 / 1050	—	—	—	24-A
						Bias Detector	250●	−5.0 (approx.)	20 to 45	Plate current to be adjusted to 0.1 milliampere with no signal.							
25A6	Power Amplifier Pentode	C2	H	25.0	0.3	Class A Amplifier	95 / 160	−15.0 / −18.0	95 / 120	4.0 / 6.5	20.0 / 33.0	45000 / 42000	2000 / 2375	—	4500 / 5000	0.9 / 2.2	25A6
25A6-GT	Power Amplifier Pentode	C3	H	25.0	0.3	Class A Amplifier	For other characteristics, refer to Type 25A6.										25A6-GT
25A7-GT	Rectifier Pentode	C3	H	25.0	0.3	Pentode Unit as Class A Amplifier	100	−15.0	100	4.0	20.5	50000	1800	—	4500	0.77	25A7-GT
						Half-Wave Rectifier	Max. A-C Plate Volts (RMS), 117. Max. Peak Inverse Volts. 350.		Max. D-C Output Ma. 350. Max. Peak Plate Ma. 450.			Min. Total Effect. Supply Impedance, 15 ohms.					
25AC5-GT	High-Mu Power Amplifier Triode	C3	H	25.0	0.3	Class B Amplifier	180	0	Bias for both 25AC5-GT and 6AE5-GT developed in circuit.		4.0◆				4800	6.0	25AC5-GT
						Dynamic-Coupled Amp. With Type 6AE5-GT Driver	110					Average Plate Current of Driver = 7 milliamperes. Average Plate Current of 25AC5-GT = 45 milliamperes.			2000	2.0	
25B5	Direct-Coupled Power Amplifier	D9a	H	25.0	0.3	Amplifier	For other characteristics, refer to Type 25N6-G.										25B5
25B6-G	Power Amplifier Pentode	D10	H	25.0	0.3	Class A Amplifier	105 / 200	−16.0 / −23.0	105 / 135	2.0 / 1.8	48.0 / 62.0	15500 / 18000	—	—	1700 / 2500	2.4 / 7.1	25B6-G
25B8-GT	Triode-Pentode	C3	H	25.0	0.15	Triode Unit as Class A Amplifier	100	−1.0	—	—	0.6	75000	1500	112	—	—	25B8-GT
						Pentode Unit as Class A Amplifier	100	−3.0	100	2.0	7.6	185000	2000	—	—	—	
25C6-G	Beam Power Amplifier	D10	H	25.0	0.3	Class A Amplifier	For other characteristics, refer to Type 6Y6-G.										25C6-G
25L6	Beam Power Amplifier	C2	H	25.0	0.3	Amplifier	For other characteristics, refer to Type 50L6-GT.										25L6
25L6-GT	Beam Power Amplifier	C3	H	25.0	0.3	Amplifier	For other characteristics, refer to Type 50L6-GT.										25L6-GT
25N6-G	Direct-Coupled Power Amplifier	D9	H	25.0	0.3	Class A Amplifier	Output Triode: Plate Volts, 180; Plate Ma., 46; Load, 4000 ohms. Triode: Plate Volts, 100; Grid Volts, 0; A-F Signal Volts (Peak), 29.7; Plate Ma., 5.8. Min. Total Effective Plate-Supply Impedance per Plate, 0 ohms.									Input 3.8	25N6-G
25Y5	Rectifier-Doubler	D5	H	25.0	0.3	Half-Wave Rectifier / Voltage Doubler	Max. A-C Volts per Plate (RMS), 235. Max. D-C Output Ma per Plate, 75.		Min. Total Effective Plate-Supply Impedance per Plate, 0 ohms.								25Y5
25Z5	Rectifier-Doubler	D5	H	25.0	0.3	Half-Wave Rectifier / Voltage Doubler	For other ratings, refer to Type 25Z6.										25Z5
25Z6	Vacuum Rectifier-Doublers	C2	H	25.0	0.3	Half-Wave Rectifier	Max. A-C Volts per Plate (RMS), 117. Max. D-C Output Ma. 75.		Min. Total Effective Plate-Supply Impedance: Half-Wave, 30 ohms; Full-Wave, 15 ohms.								25Z6
25Z6-GT		C3	H	25.0	0.3	Half-Wave Rectifier	Max. A-C Volts per Plate (RMS), 235. Max. D-C Output Ma per Plate. 75.		Min. Total Effect. Supply Imped. per Plate: Up to 117 volts, 15 ohms; at 150 volts, 40 ohms; at 235 volts, 100 ohms.								25Z6-GT
26	Amplifier Triode	D12	F	1.5	1.05	Class A Amplifier	90 / 180	−7.0 / −14.5	—	—	2.9 / 6.2	8900 / 7300	935 / 1150	8.3 / 8.3	—	—	26

Reproduced with permission of RCA Corporation.

RCA Type	Name	Tube Dimensions	Cathode Type and Rating C.T.	Volts	Amp.	Use	Plate Supply Volts	Grid Bias Volts	Screen Supply Volts	Screen Current Ma.	Plate Current Ma.	AC Plate Resistance Ohms	Transconductance (Grid-plate) µmhos	Amplification Factor	Load for Stated Power Output Ohms	Power Output Watts	RCA Type
27	Detector★ Amplifier Triode	D5	C.T.	2.5	1.75	Class A Amplifier	135 250	−9.0 −21.0	—	—	4.5 5.2	9000 9250	1000 975	9.0 9.0	—	—	27
						Bias Detector	250	(−30.0) approx.	—	—	Plate current to be adjusted to 0.2 milliampere with no signal.						
30	Detector★ Amplifier Triode	D6	D.C.-F	2.0	0.06	Amplifier	For other characteristics, refer to Type 1H4-G.										30
31	Power Amplifier Triode	D6	D.C.-F	2.0	0.13	Class A Amplifier	135 180	−22.5 −30.0	—	—	8.0 12.3	4100 3600	925 1050	3.8 3.8	7000 5700	0.185 0.375	31
32	RF Amplifier Tetrode	E1	D.C.-F	2.0	0.06	Screen-Grid RF Amplifier	135 180	−3.0 −3.0	67.5 67.5	0.4 0.4	1.7 1.7	950000 1.0+§	640 650	—	—	—	32
		E1				Bias Detector	180▼	(−6.0) approx.	67.5	—	Plate current to be adjusted to 0.2 milliampere with no signal.						
32L7-GT	Rectifier-Beam Power Amplifier	C3	H	32.5	0.3	Amplifier Unit as Class A Amplifier	90 90	−5.0 −7.0	90 90	3.0 2.0	38.0 27.0	15000 17000	6000 4800	—	2600 2600	0.8 1.0	32L7-GT
						Half-Wave Rectifier	Maximum A-C Plate Voltage............125 Volts, RMS Maximum D-C Output Current.........60 Milliamperes.										
33	Power Amplifier Pentode	D12	D.C.-F	2.0	0.26	Class A Amplifier	180	−18.0	180	5.0	22.0	55000	1700	—	6000	1.5	33
34	Supercontrol RF Amplifier Pentode	E1	D.C.-F	2.0	0.06	Screen-Grid RF Amplifier	135 180	−3.0 min.	67.5 67.5	1.0 1.0	2.8 2.8	600000 1.0§	600 620	—	—	—	34
35	Supercontrol RF Amplifier Pentode	E1	H	2.5	1.75	Screen-Grid RF Amplifier	180 250	−3.0 min.	90 90	2.5* 2.5*	6.3 6.5	300000 400000	1020 1050	—	—	—	35
35A5	Beam Power Amplifier	C8	H	35.0	0.15	Single-Tube Class A Amplifier	For other characteristics, refer to Type 35L6-GT.										35A5
35B5	Beam Power Amplifier	B1a	H	35.0	0.15	Class A Amplifier	110	−7.5	110	3.0	40	—	5800	—	2500	1.5	35B5
35L6-GT	Beam Power Amplifier	C3	H	35.0	0.15	Single-Tube Class A Amplifier	110 200	−7.5 −8.0	110 110	3.0 2.0	40.0 41.0	14000 40000	5800 5900	—	2500 4500	1.5 3.3	35L6-GT
35W4	Half-Wave Rectifier§ Heater Tap for Pilot	B1a	H	35.0	0.15	With Capacitive-Input Filter	Max. A-C Plate Volts (RMS), 117. Min. Total Effect. Plate-Supply Impedance, 15 ohms. Max. D-C Output Ma.: With Pilot and Shunt Res., 60; Without Pilot, 100										35W4
35Y4	Half-Wave Rectifier§	C8	H	35.0	0.15	With Capacitive-Input Filter	For other characteristics, refer to Type 35W4.										35Y4
35Z3	Half-Wave Rectifier	C8	H	35.0	0.15	With Capacitive-Input Filter	For other ratings, refer to Type 35Z4-GT.										35Z3
35Z4-GT	Half-Wave Rectifier	C8	H	35.0	0.15	With Capacitive-Input Filter	Max. A-C Plate Volts (RMS), 235. Min. Total Effective Plate-Supply Impedance: Up to 117 volts, 15 ohms; at 235 volts, 100 ohms. Max. D-C Output Ma., 100.										35Z4-GT
35Z5-GT	Half-Wave Rectifier Heater Tap for Pilot§	C3	H	35.0	0.15	With Capacitive-Input Filter	Max. A-C Plate Volts (RMS), 235. Min. Total Effect. Plate-Supply Imped.: Up to 117 volts, 15 ohms; at 235 volts, 100 ohms. Max. D-C Output Ma.: With Pilot and Shunt Res., 60; Without Pilot, 100.										35Z5-GT

Type	Classification	Base	Heater	Heater Volts	Heater Amps	Class of Service	Plate Volts	Grid Volts	Screen Volts	Screen Ma.	Plate Ma.	Plate Resistance (Ohms)	Transconductance (Micromhos)	Amplification Factor	Load Resistance (Ohms)	Power Output (Watts)	Type
36	RF Amplifier Tetrode	D8	H	6.3	0.3	Screen-Grid RF Amplifier Bias Detector	100/250 100@/250@	−1.5/−3.0 −5.0/−8.0	55/90 55/90	1.7*	1.8/3.2	550000/550000	850/1080	—	—	—	36
						Grid-bias values are approximate. Plate current to be adjusted to 0.1 milliampere with no signal.											
37	Detector★ Amplifier Triode	D8	H	6.3	0.3	Class A Amplifier Bias Detector	90/250 90/250	−6.0/−18.0 −10.0/−28.0			2.5/7.5	11500/8400	800/1100	9.2/9.2	—	—	37
						Grid-bias values are approximate. Plate current to be adjusted to 0.2 milliampere with no signal.											
38	Power Amplifier Pentode	D8	H	6.3	0.3	Class A Amplifier	100/250	−9.0/−25.0	100/250	1.2/3.8	7.0/22.0	140000/100000	875/1200	—	15000/10000	0.27/2.50	38
39/44	Supercontrol RF Amplifier Pentode	D8	H	6.3	0.3	Class A Amplifier	90/90	(−3.0) min.	90/90	1.6/1.4	5.6/5.8	400000/1.0‡	1000/1050	—	—	—	39/44
40	Voltage Amplifier Triode	D12	D.C./F	5.0	0.25	Class A Amplifier	135▲/180▲	−1.5/−3.0		0.2/0.2	0.2/0.2	150000/150000	200/200	30/30	—	—	40
41	Power Amplifier Pentode	D5	H	6.3	0.4	Amplifier	For other characteristics, refer to Type 6K6-GT.										41
42	Power Amplifier Pentode	D12	H	6.3	0.7	Amplifier	For other characteristics, refer to Type 6F6-G.										42
43	Power Amplifier Pentode	D12	H	25.0	0.3	Amplifier	For other characteristics, refer to Type 25A6-GT.										43
45	Power Amplifier Triode	D12	F	2.5	1.5	Class A Amplifier Push-Pull Class AB₁ Amplifier	180/275 275/275	−31.5/−56.0 Cath. Bias, 775 ohms 68.0 volts, fixed bias			31.0/36.0 36.0‡	1650/1700	2125/2050	3.5/3.5	2700/4600 5060/3200	0.82/2.00 12.0†/18.0†	45
45Z3	Half-Wave Rectifier	B0	H	45.0	0.075	Half-Wave Rectifier	Max. A-C Plate Volts (RMS), 117 Max. Peak Inverse Volts, 350			Max. D-C Output Ma. 65 Max. Peak Plate Ma. 390							45Z3
45Z5-GT	Half-Wave Rectifier Heater Tap for Pilot ‡	C3	H	45.0	0.15	With Capacitive-Input Filter	For other ratings, refer to Type 35Z5 GT. Max. Total Effect. Plate-Supply Imped. 15 ohms.										45Z5-GT
46	Dual-Grid Power Amplifier	E3	F	2.5	1.75	Class A Amplifier Class B Amplifier◆	250 300/400	−33.0 0/0		6.0	22.0 8.0‡/12.0‡	2380	2350	5.6	6400 5200/5800	1.25 16.0†/20.0†	46
47	Power Amplifier Pentode	E3	F	2.5	1.75	Class A Amplifier	250	−16.5	250	6.0	31.0	60000	2500	—	7000	2.7	47
48	Power Amplifier Tetrode	E3	D.C./H	30.0	0.4	Tetrode Tetrode Push-Pull Class A Amplifier	96/125 125	−19.0/−20.0 −20.0	96/100 100	9.0/9.5	52.0/56.0 100.0‡	3800/3900		—	1500/1500 3000	2.0/2.5 5.0†	48
49	Dual-Grid Power Amplifier	D12	D.C./F	2.0	0.12	Class A Amplifier Class B Amplifier◆	135/180 180	−20.0 0		100.0‡	6.0/4.0‡	4175/1125		4.7	11000/12000	0.17/3.5†	49
50	Power Amplifier Triode	F1a	F	7.5	1.25	Class A Amplifier	300/400/450	−54.0/−70.0/−84.0			35.0/55.0/55.0	2000/1800/1800	1900/2100/2100	3.8/3.8/3.8	4600/3670/4350	1.6/3.4/4.6	50
50A5	Beam Power Amplifier	C8	H	50.0	0.15		For other characteristics, refer to Type 50L6-GT.										50A5
50B5	Beam Power Amplifier	B1a	H	50.0	0.15	Class A Amplifier	110	−7.5	110	4	49	10000	7500	—	2500	1.9	50B5

RCA Type	Name	Tube Dimensions	Cathode C.T.	Cathode Volts	Cathode Amp.	Use	Plate Supply Volts	Grid Bias Volts	Screen Supply Volts	Screen Current Ma.	Plate Current Ma.	AC Plate Resistance Ohms	Transconductance (Grid-plate) μmhos	Amplification Factor	Load for Stated Power Output Ohms	Power Output Watts	RCA Type
50L6-GT	Beam Power Amplifier	C3	H	50.0	0.15	Single-Tube Class A Amplifier	110 / 200	−7.5 / −8.0	110 / 110	4.0 / 2.0	49.0 / 50.0	13000 / 30000	9000 / 9500	—	2000 / 3000	2.1 / 4.3	50L6-GT
50Y6-GT	Rectifier-Doubler	C3	H	50.0	0.15	Rectifier-Doubler	For other ratings, refer to Type 2526.										50Y6-GT
5027-G	Rectifier-Doubler Heater Tap for Pilot ‡	D3	H	50.0	0.15	Voltage Doubler	Max. A-C Volts per Plate (RMS), 117; Max. D-C Output Ma., 65; Min. Total Effective Plate-Supply Impedance: 15 ohms.										5027-G
						Half-Wave Rectifier	M·† A-C Volts per Plate (RMS), 235; Max. D-C Output Ma. per Plate, 65; Min. Total Effective Plate-Supply Impedance per Plate: Up to 117 volts, 15 ohms; at 235 volts, 100 ohms.										
53	Twin-Triode Amplifier	D12	H	2.5	2.0	Amplifier	For other characteristics, refer to Type 6N7-GT.										53
55	Duplex-Diode Triode	D9	H	2.5	1.0	Triode Unit as Amplifier	For other characteristics, refer to Type 85.										55
56	Detector Amplifier Triode★	D5	H	2.5	1.0	Amplifier Detector	For other characteristics, refer to Type 76.										56
57	Triple-Grid Detector Amplifier	D13	H	2.5	1.0	Amplifier Detector	For other characteristics, refer to Type 6J7.										57
58	Triple-Grid Supercontrol Amplifier	D13	H	2.5	1.0	Amplifier Mixer	For other characteristics, refer to Type 6U7-G.										58
59	Triple-Grid Power Amplifier	E3	H	2.5	2.0	Triode¶ Class A Amplifier	250	−28.0	—	—	26.0	2300	2600	6.0	5000	1.25	59
						Pentode** Class A Amplifier	250	−18.0	250	9.0	35.0	55000	2500	—	6000	3.0	
						Triode⊕ Class B Amplifier	300 / 400	0 / 0	—	—	20.0◊ / 26.0◊	—	—	—	4600 / 6000	15.0† / 20.0†	
70L7-GT	Rectifier-Beam Power Amplifier	C5b	H	70.0	0.15	Amplifier Unit as Class A Amplifier	110	−7.5	110	3.0	40.0	15000	7500	—	2000	1.8	70L7-GT
						Half-Wave Rectifier	Max. A-C Plate Volts (RMS), 117; Max. Peak Inverse Volts, 350; Max. D-C Output Ma., 70; Max. Peak Plate Ma., 420; Min. Total Effect. Plate-Supply Imped., 15 ohms.										
71-A	Power Amplifier Triode	D12	F	5.0	0.25	Class A Amplifier	90 / 180	−16.5 / −40.5	—	—	10.0 / 20.0	2170 / 1750	1400 / 1700	3.0 / 3.0	3000 / 4800	0.125 / 0.790	71-A
75	Duplex-Diode High-Mu Triode	D9	H	6.3	0.3	Amplifier	For other characteristics, refer to Type 6SQ7.										75
76	Detector Amplifier Triode★	D5	H	6.3	0.3	Class A Amplifier	250	−13.5	—	—	5.0	9500	1450	13.8	—	—	76
						Bias Detector	250	−20.0 (approx.)	Plate current to be adjusted to 0.2 milliampere with no signal.								
77	Triple-Grid Detector Amplifier	D9	H	6.3	0.3	Class A Amplifier	100 / 250	−1.5 / −3.0	60 / 100	0.4 / 0.5	1.7 / 2.3	600000 / 1.0+§	1100 / 1250	—	—	—	77
						Bias Detector	250	−1.95	50	Cathode current 0.65 ma.		Plate Resistor, 250000 ohms. Grid Resistor,** 250000 ohms.					

Reproduced with permission of RCA Corporation.

Type	Class	Base	Cath.	Fil./Heater Volts	Amps	Operation	Plate Volts	Grid Volts	Screen Volts	Plate Ma.	Plate Res.	Transcond.	Amp. Factor	Load (ohms)	Power Output (W)	Notes	Type
78	Triple-Grid Supercontrol Amplifier	D6	H	6.3	0.3	Amplifier Mixer	180 / 250	0 / 0								For other characteristics, refer to Type 6K7.	78
79	Twin-Triode Amplifier	D6	H	6.3	0.6	Class B Amplifier	—	—						7000 / 14000	5.5 / 8.0	Power Output is for one tube at stated plate-to-plate load.	79
80	Full-Wave Rectifier	D12	F	5.0	2.0											For other ratings, refer to Type 5Y3-GT.	80
81	Half-Wave Rectifier	F1	F	7.5	1.25		Max. A-C Plate Volts (RMS), 700; Max. Peak Inverse Volts, 2000			Max. D-C Output Ma., 85; Max. Peak Plate Ma., 500							81
82	Full-Wave Rectifier	D12	F	2.5	3.0	With Capacitive-Input Filter	Max. A-C Volts per Plate (RMS), 450; Max. Peak Inverse Volts, 1550			Max. D-C Output Ma., 115; Max. Peak Plate Ma., 600						Min. Total Effect. Supply Imped. per Plate, 50 ohm.	82
						With Inductive-Input Filter	Max. A-C Volts per Plate (RMS), 550; Max. Peak Inverse Volts, 1550			Max. D-C Output Ma., 115; Max. Peak Plate Ma., 600						Min. Value of Input Choke, 6 henries	
83	Full-Wave Rectifier	E3	F	5.0	3.0	With Capacitive-Input Filter	Max. A-C Volts per Plate (RMS), 450; Max. Peak Inverse Volts, 1550			Max. D-C Output Ma., 225; Max. Peak Plate Ma., 1000						Min. Total Effect. Supply Imped. per Plate, 50 ohm.	83
						With Inductive-Input Filter	Max. A-C Volts per Plate (RMS), 550; Max. Peak Inverse Volts, 1550			Max. D-C Output Ma., 225; Max. Peak Plate Ma., 1000						Min. Value of Input Choke, 3 henries	
83-v	Full-Wave Rectifier	D12	H	5.0	2.0											For other ratings, refer to Type 5V4-G.	83-v
84/6Z4	Full-Wave Rectifier	D6	H	6.3	0.5	With Capacitive-Input Filter	Max. A-C Volts per Plate (RMS), 325; Max. Peak Inverse Volts, 1250			Max. D-C Output Ma., 60; Max. Peak Plate Ma., 180						Min. Total Effect. Supply Imped. per Plate, 150 ohm.	84/6Z4
						With Inductive-Input Filter	Max. A-C Volts per Plate (RMS), 450; Max. Peak Inverse Volts, 1250			Max. D-C Output Ma., 60; Max. Peak Plate Ma., 180						Min. Value of Input Choke, 10 henries	
85	Duplex-Diode Triode	D9	H	6.3	0.3	Triode Unit as Class A Amplifier	135 / 250	−10.5 / −20.0		3.7 / 8.0	11000 / 7500	750 / 1100	8.3 / 8.3	25000 / 20000	0.075 / 0.350		85
89	Triple-Grid Power Amplifier	D8	H	6.3	0.4	As Triode / Class A Amplifier	160 / 250	−20.0 / −31.0		17.0 / 32.0	3300 / 2600	1425 / 1800	4.7 / 4.7	7000 / 5500	0.30 / 0.90		89
						As Pentode / Class A Amplifier	100 / 250	−10.0 / −25.0	100 / 250	9.5 / 32.0	104000 / 70000	1200 / 1800	1.6 / 5.0	10700 / 6750	0.33 / 3.40		
						As Triode / Class B Amplifier	180	0		6.0◊	—	—		13600 / 9400	2.50† / 3.50†		
V-99 / X-99	Detector Amplifier Triodes	C4 / D1	D.C. / F	3.3	0.063	Class A Amplifier	90	−4.5		2.5	15500	425	6.6				V-99 / X-99
112-A	Detector Amplifier Triode	D12	D.C. / F	5.0	0.25	Class A Amplifier	90 / 180	−4.5 / −13.5		5.0 / 7.7	5400 / 4700	1575 / 1800	8.5 / 8.5				112-A
117L7/M7-GT	Rectifier-Beam Power Amplifier	C9b	H	117	0.09	Amplifier Unit as Class A Amplifier	105	−5.2	105	43.0	17000	5300	4.0	4000	0.85		117L7/M7-GT
						Half-Wave Rectifier	Max. A-C Plate Volts (RMS), 117; Max. Peak Inverse Volts, 350			Max. D-C Output Ma., 75; Max. Peak Plate Ma., 450						Min. Total Effect. Plate-Supply Imped., 15 ohms.	
117N7-GT	Rectifier-Beam Power Amplifier	C9b	H	117	0.09	Amplifier Unit as Class A Amplifier	100	−6.0	100	51.0	16000	7000	5.0	3000	1.2		117N7-GT
						Half-Wave Rectifier	Max. A-C Plate Volts (RMS), 117; Max. Peak Inverse Volts, 350			Max. D-C Output Ma., 75; Max. Peak Plate Ma., 450						Min. Total Effect. Plate-Supply Impedance, 15 ohms. For other characteristics, refer to Type 117L7/M7-GT.	
117P7-GT	Rectifier-Beam Power Amplifier	C9b	H	117	0.09	Amplifier Unit as Class A Amplifier / Half-Wave Rectifier										For other characteristics, refer to Type 117L7/M7-GT.	117P7-GT

RCA Type	Name	Tube Dimensions	Cathode Type and Rating — C.T.	Volts	Amp.	Use (Values to right give operating conditions and characteristics for indicated typical use)	Plate Supply Volts	Grid Bias Volts	Screen Supply Volts	Screen Current Ma.	Plate Current Ma.	AC Plate Resistance Ohms	Transconductance (Grid-plate) μmhos	Amplification Factor	Load for Stated Power Output Ohms	Power Output Watts
117Z3	Half-Wave Rectifier	B1a	H	117	0.04	With Capacitive-Input Filter	Max. A-C Plate Volts (RMS), 117 ; Max. Peak Inverse Volts, 330				Max. D-C Output Ma. 90 Max. Peak Plate Ma., 340					Min. Total Effect. Plate-Supply Imped., 15 ohms
117Z6-GT	Rectifier-Doubler	C3	H	117	0.075	Voltage Doubler	Max. A-C Volts per Plate (RMS), 117 Max. D-C Output Ma., 60								Min. Total Effective Plate-Supply Impedance per Plate: Half-Wave, 30 ohms; Full-Wave, 15 ohms	
						Half-Wave Rectifier	Max. A-C Volts per Plate (RMS), 235 Max. D-C Output Ma. per Plate, 60								Min. Total Effect. Supply Imped. per Plate: Up to 117 volts, 15 ohms; at 150 volts, 40 ohms; at 235 volts, 100 ohms.	
183/ 483	Power Amplifier Triode	D12	F	5.0	1.25	Class A Amplifier	250	−60.0	—	—	30.0	1750	1700	3.0	5000	1.8
485	Detector Amplifier Triode	D5	H	3.0	1.25	Class A Amplifier	180	− 9.0	—	—	5.8	8900	1400	12.5	—	—

Three vertical rules before or after type No. = Miniature type.

Two vertical rules before or after type No. = Metal type.

One vertical rule before or after type No. = GT or other larger glass type.

Light Face = Discontinued type.

Note 1: Subscript 1 on class of amplifier service (as AB₁) indicates that grid current does not flow during any part of input cycle.

Note 2: Subscript 2 on class of amplifier service (as AB₂) indicates that grid current flows during some part of input cycle.

■ Supply voltage applied through 20000-ohm voltage-dropping resistor.

▲ Grids #2 and #4 are screen. Grid #1 is signal-input control grid.

★ For Grid-leak Detection—plate volts 45, grid return to + filament or to cathode.

♣ For two tubes.

▦ Either ac or dc may be used on filament or heater, except as specifically noted. For use of dc on ac filament types, decrease stated grid volts by ½ (approx.) of filament voltage.

● 50000 ohms.

§ Megohms.

♦ Obtained preferably by using 70000-ohm voltage-dropping resistor in series with 90-volt supply;

** For grid of following tube.

✕ Applied through plate resistor of 250000 ohms.

▲▲ Both grids connected together; likewise both cathodes

◉ Grids #3 and #5 are screen. Grid No. 4 is signal-input grid.

▲ Grids #2 and #4 are screen. Grid #3 is signal-input control grid.

† Power output is for two tubes at stated plate-to-plate load.

► Mercury-Vapor Type.

¶ Grid #1 is control grid. Grids #2 and #3 tied to plate.

** Grid #1 is control grid. Grid #2 is screen. Grid #3 tied to cathode.

● Grids #1 and #2 connected together. Grid #3 tied to plate.

♥ Applied through plate resistor of 100000 ohms.

♯ Panel lamp section is between pins 2 and 3.

● Applied through plate resistor of 250000 ohms or 500-henry choke shunted by 0.25-megohm resistor.

• Maximum.

✝ Grids #2 and #3 tied to plate.

○ Both grids connected together; likewise, both plates.

¶ For signal-input control-grid (#1); control-grid #3 bias, −3 volts.

Index

Index

245

Other Bestsellers From TAB